Y0-AQY-713

St. Benedicts Prep.
520 M.L. King Blvd.
Newark, NJ 07102

LIBRARY ONLY

Raintree Steck-Vaughn

Illustrated
SCIENCE
ENCYCLOPEDIA

Volume
21

TEX – VIO

RADEL LIBRARY
St. Benedicts Prep.
520 M.L. King Blvd.
Newark, NJ 07102

RSVP
**RAINTREE
STECK-VAUGHN**
P U B L I S H E R S
The Steck-Vaughn Company

Austin, Texas

Copyright © 1997 Steck-Vaughn Company

Some drawn art copyright © Andromeda Oxford Ltd.
and Macdonald Young Books Ltd.
For photographic credits, see Volume 23.

All rights reserved. No part of the material protected by this copyright may be reproduced in any form by any means, electronic or mechanical, including photocopying, recording, or by any information storage and retrieval system, without permission in writing from the copyright owner. Requests for permission to make copies of any part of the work should be mailed to: Copyright Permissions, Steck-Vaughn Company, P.O. Box 26015, Austin, Texas 78755.

Published by Raintree Steck-Vaughn Publishers, an imprint of Steck-Vaughn Company.

Executive Editor	Diane Sharpe
Senior Editor	Anne Souby
Design Manager	Joyce Spicer

This edition edited and designed by Andromeda Oxford Ltd.

Andromeda Editorial and Design

Project Manager	Julia Roles
Editorial Manager	Jenny Fry
Design	TT Designs, T&S Truscott
Cover Design	John Barker

Library of Congress Cataloging-in-Publication Data
Raintree Steck-Vaughn illustrated science encyclopedia.
      p.   cm.
    Includes bibliographical references and index.
    Summary: A twenty-four volume set containing brief articles on science topics.
    ISBN 0-8172-3943-X (set)
    ISBN 0-8172-3939-1 (Volume 21)
    1. Science—Encyclopedias, Juvenile. [1. Science—Encyclopedias.]   I. Raintree Steck-Vaughn Publishers.
Q121.R354   1997
503—dc20   96-11078
                                         CIP
                                         AC

Printed and Bound in the United States of America.
1 2 3 4 5 6 7 8 9 10 IP 00 99 98 97 96

USING THE RAINTREE STECK-VAUGHN ILLUSTRATED SCIENCE ENCYCLOPEDIA

You are living in a world in which science, technology, and nature are very important. You see something about science almost every day. It might be on television, in the newspaper, in a book at school, or some other place. Often, you want more information about what you see.

The *Raintree Steck-Vaughn Illustrated Science Encyclopedia* will help you find what you want to know. It contains information on many science subjects. You may want to find out about computers, the environment, space exploration, biology, agriculture, or mathematics, for example. They are all in the *Raintree Steck-Vaughn Illustrated Science Encyclopedia.* There are many, many other subjects covered as well.

There are twenty-four volumes in the encyclopedia. The articles, which are called entries, are in alphabetical order through the first twenty-two volumes. On the spine of each volume, below the volume number, are some letters. The letters above the line are the first three letters of the first entry in that volume. The letters below the line are the first three letters of the last entry in that volume. In Volume 1, for example, you see that the first entry begins with **AAR** and that the last entry begins with **ANT**. Using the letters makes it easy to find the volume you need.

In Volume 23, there are three special features—reference charts and tables, a bibliography, and an index. In Volume 24, there are interesting projects that you can do on your own. The projects are fun to do, and they help you discover and understand important science principles. Many can give you ideas that can help you develop your own science fair projects.

Main Entries There are two kinds of main entries in the *Raintree Steck-Vaughn Illustrated Science Encyclopedia.* Many of the entries are major topics that are spread over several pages. The titles of these entries are shown at the top of the page in a yellow box. Other entries required less space to cover the topic fully. The titles of these main entries are printed in capital letters. They look like this: **ABALONE.** At the beginning of some entries, you will see a phonetic pronunciation of the entry title, such as (ăb′ ə lō′ nē).

In the front of each volume, there is a pronunciation key. Use it the same way you use your dictionary's pronunciation key.

Cross-References Within the main entries are cross-references referring to other entries in the encyclopedia. Within an entry, they look like this: (see MAMMAL). At the end of an entry, they look like this: *See also* HYENA. These cross-references tell you where to find other helpful information on the subject you are reading about.

Projects At the end of some entries, you will see this symbol: PROJECT 1. It tells you which projects related to that entry are in Volume 24.

Illustrations There are thousands of photographs, drawings, graphs, diagrams, tables, and other illustrations in the *Raintree Steck-Vaughn Illustrated Science Encyclopedia.* They will help you better understand the entries you read. Captions describe the illustrations. Many of the illustrations also have labels that point out important parts.

Activities Some main entries include activities presented in a special box. These activities are short projects that give you a chance to work with science on your own.

Index In Volume 23, the index lists every main entry by volume and page number. Many subjects that are not main entries are also listed in the index, as well as the illustrations, projects, activities, and reference charts and tables.

Bibliography In Volume 23, there is also a bibliography for students. The books in this list are on a variety of topics and can supplement what you have learned in the *Raintree Steck-Vaughn Illustrated Science Encyclopedia.*

The *Raintree Steck-Vaughn Illustrated Science Encyclopedia* was designed especially for you, the student. It is a source of knowledge for the world of science, technology, and nature. Enjoy it!

PRONUNCIATION KEY

Each symbol has the same sound as the darker letters in the sample words.

ə	balloon, ago	îr	deer, pier	r	root, tire
ă	map, have	j	join, germ	s	so, press
ā	day, made	k	king, ask	sh	shoot, machine
âr	care, bear	l	let, cool	t	to, stand
ä	father, car	m	man, same	th	thin, death
b	ball, rib	n	no, turn	*th*	then, this
ch	choose, nature	ng	bring, long	ŭ	up, cut
d	did, add	ŏ	odd, pot	ûr	urge, hurt
ĕ	bell, get	ō	cone, know	v	view, give
ē	sweet, easy	ô	all, saw	w	wood, glowing
f	fan, soft	oi	boy, boil	y	yes, year
g	good, big	ou	now, loud	z	zero, raise
h	hurt, ahead	ŏŏ	good, took	zh	leisure, vision
ĭ	rip, ill	ōō	boot, noon	'	strong accent
ī	side, sky	p	part, scrap	´	weak accent

GUIDE TO MEASUREMENT ABBREVIATIONS

All measurements in the *Raintree Steck-Vaughn Illustrated Science Encyclopedia* are given in both the customary system and the metric system [in brackets like these]. Following are the abbreviations used for various units of measure.

Customary Units of Measure

mi. = miles	cu. yd. = cubic yards
m.p.h. = miles per hour	cu. ft. = cubic feet
yd. = yards	cu. in. = cubic inches
ft. = feet	gal. = gallons
in. = inches	pt. = pints
sq. mi. = square miles	qt. = quarts
sq. yd. = square yards	lb. = pounds
sq. ft. = square feet	oz. = ounces
sq. in. = square inches	fl. oz. = fluid ounces
cu. mi. = cubic miles	°F = degrees Fahrenheit

Metric Units of Measure

km = kilometers	cu. km = cubic kilometers
kph = kilometers per hour	cu. m = cubic meters
m = meters	cu. cm = cubic centimeters
cm = centimeters	ml = milliliters
mm = millimeters	kg = kilograms
sq. km = square kilometers	g = grams
sq. m = square meters	mg = milligrams
sq. cm = square centimeters	°C = degrees Celsius

For information on how to convert customary measurements to metric measurements, see the Metric Conversions table in Volume 23.

Traditionally, a textile (tĕks′tīl′) is any woven fabric made from yarn. Yarn is made of twisted fibers (see FIBER). Twisting fibers into yarn is called spinning. The process of interlacing, or connecting, yarns into a textile is called weaving. Weaving is done on a machine called a loom. Today, fabrics that are made by methods other than weaving are also called textiles. For example, the process of knitting involves moving a single yarn by means of needles to produce a textile. The textile called lace is made not only by interlacing but also by twisting yarns around one another. Felt is produced by pounding a mass of hot, wet fibers together.

Textiles are often grouped by the type of fiber from which they are made. Natural fibers include cotton, linen, wool, and silk. These fibers are taken from the cotton plant, the stalk of the flax plant, the fleece of the sheep, and the cocoon of the silkworm, respectively. Synthetic (human-made) fibers are obtained by processing wood, cotton, or chemicals. Synthetic fibers include acrylics, nylon, polyesters, rayon, and fibers made from glass (see ACRYLIC; COTTON; FIBERGLASS; NYLON; POLYMER; RAYON; WOOL).

Woven textiles are grouped according to the pattern of weave. The three basic weaves are called plain, twill, and satin. In the plain weave, the yarns are evenly woven over and under in both directions. Cheesecloth, flannel, and muslin are among the fabrics made using plain weave. The yarns of a fabric made using twill weave form a diagonal pattern. Twill-weave fabrics include denim, herringbone, and worsted gabardine. Satin weaves are shiny, smooth weaves that have no distinct diagonal pattern. Some undergarments are made in the satin weave.

A textile may be all of one fiber, such as wool, or of a combination of fibers, such as wool and Orlon. Orlon is a synthetic fiber.

FIBERS

All textiles are made from fibers. One of the oldest animal fibers is wool, obtained from the fleece of sheep (above). Linen, a vegetable fiber, comes from the stalks of flax plants (left).

HARVESTING COTTON
In the United States, cotton bolls are harvested using machines. But in Central America and Asia, cotton is often still picked by hand.

Preparing fibers Cotton is produced in seed pods called bolls. After picking, the cotton is separated from the seeds in machines called gins. Gins have rotating brushes or fluted (grooved) rollers. After the seeds have been removed, the fibers are beaten to loosen them. They are then blown against a drum with tiny holes. This drum removes dirt and short fibers. The remaining long fibers are rolled into flat sheets. The fibers are then straightened out by a process called carding. This process also twists the fibers into a loose rope. The loose ropes are then drawn into longer, finer strands called rovings. The rovings are ready for spinning.

To make linen, the flax plants are combed to remove seeds. The fibers are separated by partly rotting the plant in water for several weeks. The stalks of the plant are then beaten in a device called a scutching machine to remove the woody parts. A hacking machine removes the shorter fibers and other material. The long fibers come out as a loose rope that is drawn out into a roving ready for spinning.

Wool sheared from a sheep contains different qualities of fibers. It is also mixed with impurities such as dirt and sweat. The wool is scoured (scrubbed) in tanks of detergent to remove the impurities. The wool is then treated with hydrochloric acid and heated to remove any further impurities. Wool is then carded, combed, and drawn out.

The silkworm spins long threads called filaments, which it wraps into a cocoon (see COCOON). The cocoon is heated to kill the silkworm. The filaments are unwound from the cocoon and wound onto reels. Several filaments are twisted into a yarn by a process called throwing. Any short or broken fibers are chopped up and turned into spun silk by processes like those used for cotton or wool.

Synthetic fibers are produced as continuous filaments. Like silk, these filaments are thrown into yarns.

Spinning and weaving Before spinning, the roving, a thin strand of fibers, is drawn to the desired thickness by passing it through rollers. The roving is then twisted on a spinning frame to form yarn.

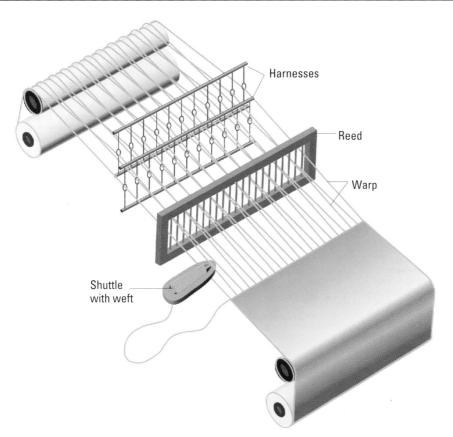

Harnesses

Reed

Warp

Shuttle
with weft

LOOM PRINCIPLE

At left is a diagram of a hand loom. A yarn called the weft is passed crosswise through multiple lengthwise yarns called the warp. The warp yarns are separated by lifting one harness at a time, which allows the weft shuttle to be passed between the warp yarns. The newly woven yarn is pushed into place by the reed.

HAND LOOM

During the colonial period in America, many families had their own hand looms like this one below.

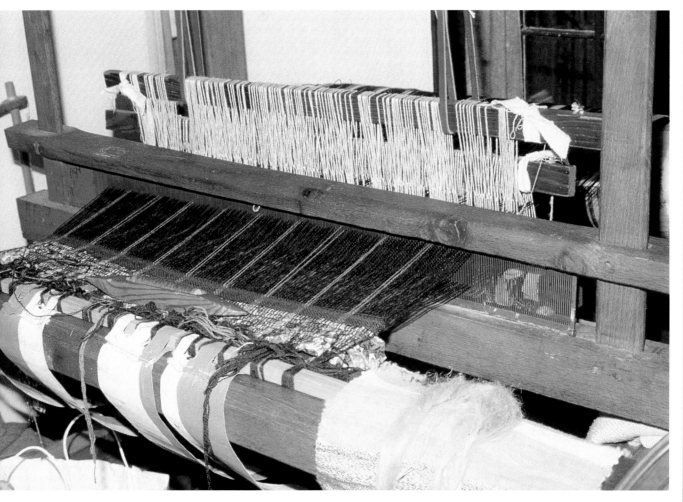

MODERN LOOM
Once they are set up, modern looms run automatically at high speed. This unit functions as two looms side by side.

Fabric is woven from two sets of yarns at right angles. One set of yarns, the warp, is placed and held tight on a loom. The other set of yarns, the weft, is threaded through the warp by means of a shuttle. Alternate yarns of the warp are lifted and lowered so the shuttle can pass between them. After the weft yarn has passed, the newly woven row is pushed into place by a comb-shaped device called a reed. These processes are repeated for each weft yarn until the fabric is completed. The edges of the fabric, called selvages, are strengthened by doubling the yarn or using a stronger yarn.

Finishing operations Fabrics are usually bleached to improve the whiteness and to prepare them for dyeing (see DYE). A variety of dyes and dyeing methods are available. Different dyes are suited to particular types of fabrics. The color may also be placed on the fabric by printing. Textile printing is usually done with large rollers on which a pattern or design has been deeply engraved. A separate roller is used for each color in the design. Screen printing is performed with a stencil on which the design is cut out. When the stencil is placed on the fabric, the dye colors only the cut-out areas.

Once a textile has been dyed or printed, it may go through one or more finishing processes. Some fabrics are treated to keep them from creasing or fading. Some fabrics are coated with resins to give a shiny appearance and often to make them crease resistant (see RESIN). Some textiles are bonded with a thin foam-rubber backing. This helps the textile keep its shape. Some fabrics go through a special preshrinking process. Some fabrics are coated with plastic or rubber to make waterproof items, such as place mats and boots. Other treatments can make a fabric stainproof or fireproof.

THALLUS (thăl′əs) *Thallus* is the name given to the body of seaweeds and other algae, and also to the body of some other simple organisms. The thallus is not divided into leaves, stems, and roots.

Some thalli (plural of *thallus*) are made only of one cell, while others are multicellular (having many cells). The cells of multicellular thalli are all very similar. In fungi, the thallus is called a mycelium. Some primitive liverworts have seaweedlike thalli. The more advanced forms, however, have leaves and stems containing several different kinds of cells.

See also ALGAE; CELL; FUNGUS; MOSS, LIVERWORT, HORNWORT; SEAWEED.

THERMIONIC EMISSION Thermionic emission is the emission (sending out) of electrons by a heated metal or metal-based material. Electrons are subatomic particles (particles smaller than an atom) that are found inside all atoms (see ATOM; ELECTRON). In a metal, electrons are able to break free of the metal atoms and move between the atoms. These free electrons move faster as the metal is heated. If the temperature rises enough, the electrons move so quickly that they can break through the surface of the metal. The thermionic valve, or vacuum tube, used in radio and radar sets produces electrons in this way (see VACUUM TUBE).

THERMIONIC EMISSION
A thermionic valve, or vacuum tube, makes use of thermionic emission to produce streams of electrons from a heated wire.

A television tube contains electron guns that produce electrons in the same way. In a television tube, the electrons are projected onto the front of the tube to produce the picture.

THERMISTOR (thûr′mĭs′tər) Thermistors are devices that measure very small changes in temperature. They are used in very sensitive thermometers (see TEMPERATURE; THERMOMETER). Thermistors are made of semiconducting materials (see SEMICONDUCTOR). A semiconductor is a substance that has different resistances to the passage of an electric current under different circumstances (see CURRENT, ELECTRIC; RESISTANCE, ELECTRICAL). For example, when a semiconductor is heated, its resistance decreases. Therefore, if the semiconductor in a thermistor loses some of its resistance, the thermistor registers an increase in temperature. Thermistors can measure temperature changes of less than 0.001°F [0.0005°C].

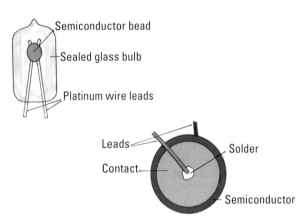

THERMISTOR
Pictured above are two kinds of thermistors—a bead thermistor (left) and a disk thermistor (right).

THERMOCOUPLE (thûr′mə kŏp′əl) A thermocouple is an electrical device that changes heat into electricity or vice versa. They are used as thermometers and to generate electricity (see THERMOMETER). A thermocouple contains two pieces of wire made from different metals, such as iron or copper. The wires are twisted together at one end to form a junction. The opposite ends are also twisted to form another junction. If one junction is heated, then a heat-generated current will flow between the free ends of the wires. The size of the voltage, or electrical potential, depends on the metals used. It also depends on the temperature difference between the junction and the free ends. If the free ends are kept at a certain temperature, then the temperature of the junction can be measured from the size of the voltage.

The voltage developed by most metals is very small. Only a few metals, such as copper and iron, give a high voltage. The voltage can be increased by joining a number of thermocouples. This arrangement is called a thermopile. A thermopile measures temperatures much more accurately than a thermocouple.

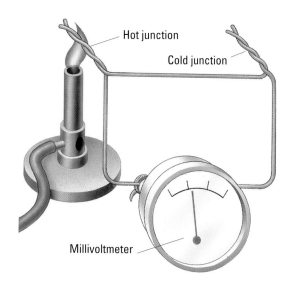

- Hot junction
- Cold junction
- Millivoltmeter

THERMOCOUPLE

A thermocouple consists of two wires made of different metals twisted together at their ends, forming junctions. If one junction is heated, an electric current flows and can be measured by a millivoltmeter. The size of the voltage is a measure of the temperature of the hot junction.

THERMODYNAMICS (thûr´mō dī năm´ĭks)

Thermodynamics is the study of the relationships between matter, heat, and other forms of energy (see ENERGY; HEAT). The principles of thermodynamics are important in all branches of science and engineering.

There are three important laws in thermodynamics. The first law has to do with the changing of energy from one form to another. It states that when one form of energy is changed into another, the amount of energy does not change. This law is known as the law of conservation of energy. For example, in a steam engine, wood, coal, or oil is burned to change water into steam (see STEAM

ENGINE). The steam then drives the engine and makes it do work. The fuel contains a large amount of chemical energy. When it burns, this energy changes into heat energy. The steam engine then changes the heat energy into mechanical energy. Chemical energy, heat energy, and mechanical energy are all different forms of energy. Part of the heat energy of the steam is changed into unwanted friction between the moving parts in the engine (see FRICTION). The total amount of energy always remains the same.

The second law of thermodynamics deals with the direction in which energy naturally flows. For example, if two bodies are at different temperatures, heat will flow naturally from the warmer body to the cooler body. The heat energy of the warmer body is being decreased. In time, the two

THERMODYNAMICS

A steam engine, like every other type of heat engine, obeys the laws of thermodynamics.

ST. BENEDICT'S PREP LIBRARY

THERMOGRAPHY

Thermography produces pictures, called thermograms, that reveal objects that give off heat. This thermogram of part of an oil refinery shows which pipes and containers hold hot gases or liquids. The lighter the color, the hotter the object is.

bodies will be at the same temperature. However, heat cannot flow naturally from the cooler body to the warmer one. To transfer heat from a cooler body to a warmer one, outside energy must be applied.

Entropy, or randomness, is a concept that is used in thermodynamics (see ENTROPY). Processes in which entropy is increased tend to happen naturally. For instance, if marbles are dropped on the floor, they scatter in a random pattern. They do not pile up neatly. Processes in which entropy is decreased do not occur naturally. To put the marbles into a neat, ordered pile, the person who collects and arranges them must apply energy.

The third law of thermodynamics is also known as the Nernst heat theorem. It says that the temperature of a body cannot decrease indefinitely. There is a temperature called absolute zero, which is -459.67°F [-273.15°C]. The temperature of a body can never be brought down to absolute zero. *See also* ABSOLUTE ZERO.

THERMOGRAPHY Thermography is a way of converting invisible heat into a visible heat picture, known as a thermogram, which can be studied. The thermogram is created using a device called a thermograph. The thermograph senses the infrared, or heat, energy radiated naturally by all objects and converts the energy into electrical signals (see ENERGY; INFRARED RAY). The signals are displayed as pictures on a television screen where the different ranges of infrared appear as different colors or levels of brightness.

Thermography can be used to help rescue teams find people in the dark and through smoke. It is also used in industry to detect electrical faults and find leaks in insulation. Doctors use thermography to study arthritis, nerve damage, tumors, and blood circulation problems.

Thermography is also the name of a printing process that imitates deep-etched or engraved characters (see PRINTING). It is used on business cards and letterheads.

THERMOMETER

A thermometer (thər mŏm′ĭ tər) is an instrument used to measure temperature (see TEMPERATURE). Thermometers have a great variety of uses. These uses include measuring air or room temperatures and checking body temperature for a fever (see TEMPERATURE, BODY).

Liquid-in-glass thermometers The most common thermometer in the home is the liquid-in-glass thermometer. This thermometer works on the principle that liquid expands, or pushes outward, as it gets warmer (see EXPANSION). A liquid-in-glass thermometer is made of a glass tube with a small hole, or bore, through it. At the bottom of the tube is a small bulb, or reservoir. The upper end of the tube is closed. The reservoir is filled with a certain amount of a liquid. As the temperature rises, the liquid expands. The liquid stops expanding when its temperature equals the temperature of the area around it. The temperature is read from the top of the liquid.

Mercury is the most common liquid used in liquid-in-glass thermometers (see MERCURY). Mercury cannot be used to measure temperatures less than or equal to its freezing point of -38°F [-39°C]. Alcohol is also used in thermometers. It cannot be used to measure temperatures greater than or equal to its boiling point of 173°F [78.4°C]. Alcohol is sometimes dyed red or blue for use in a thermometer.

THERMOMETER TYPES

Originally, most thermometers consisted of a narrow glass tube connected to a bulb containing a liquid (usually mercury or alcohol containing a dye to make it easier to see). Modern thermometers include liquid-crystal strips (below), which change color according to the temperature, and electronic devices that give a digital display of the temperature (far right).

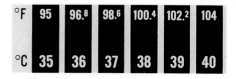

°F	95	96.8	98.6	100.4	102.2	104
°C	35	36	37	38	39	40

Bimetallic strip thermometers A bimetallic strip thermometer consists of two different metals joined together (see BIMETALLIC STRIP). When the temperature changes, the two metals expand and

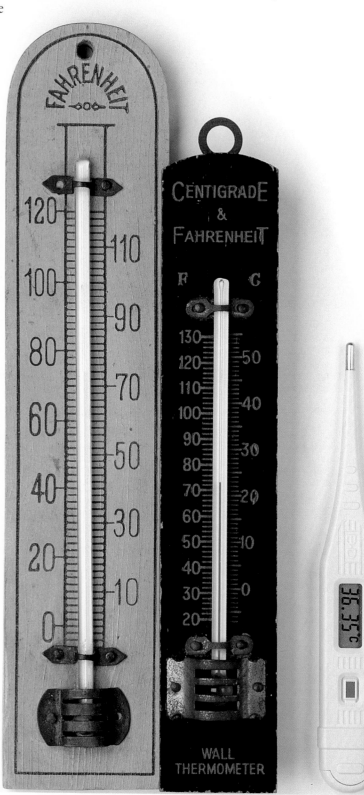

WALL THERMOMETER

contract at different rates, causing the strip to bend. The strip is attached to a pointer that indicates the temperature.

Bimetallic strip thermometers are often used in instruments called thermographs. A thermograph has a pen attached to the bimetallic strip instead of a pointer. The pen records temperatures on a chart that revolves on a drum.

Electrical thermometers

Temperatures can also be shown by electrical devices. A thermocouple changes heat into electricity and produces a voltage (see THERMOCOUPLE). The voltage varies according to the temperature. The voltage can be applied to a galvanometer, and the galvanometer's scale shows the temperature (see GALVANOMETER).

A resistance thermometer consists of a sealed tube containing tightly coiled platinum wire. The greater the temperature is, the greater the electrical

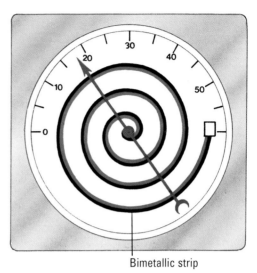

BIMETALLIC STRIP

A bimetallic strip thermometer (above) gives an approximate measure of temperature. The bimetallic strip is made of two metals. As the temperature changes, the two metals expand and contract at different rates, causing the strip to bend. The strip is attached to a pointer that indicates the temperature.

resistance of the wire. The temperature is found by measuring the resistance (see RESISTANCE, ELECTRICAL).

Other kinds of thermometers

Digital thermometers use electronic devices and circuits to measure temperature (see ELECTRONICS). In these thermometers, a slender device called a probe sends temperature readings to an integrated circuit in the form of electrical signals (see INTEGRATED CIRCUIT). The signals are changed into numbers. The numbers appear in a display window. Disposable thermometers are often used to measure body temperature. Some disposable thermometers use liquid crystals (see LCD (LIQUID CRYSTAL DISPLAY)). Most disposable thermometers are meant to be discarded after one use.

Temperature scales

Scales have been invented for the measurement of temperatures. The Celsius scale has 0° as the freezing point of water and 100° as the boiling point. The Fahrenheit scale has 32° as the freezing point of water and 212° as the boiling point. The Celsius scale is used in most scientific work. The Fahrenheit scale is chiefly used in the United States. Most other countries use the Celsius scale.

See also CELSIUS SCALE; FAHRENHEIT SCALE.

PROJECT 25, 45

Resistance coil

RESISTANCE THERMOMETER

A resistance thermometer containing tightly coiled platinum wire is shown in two views. The metallic sheath of the thermometer has been cut away to show the position of the coil inside it.

THERMOSTAT

Electric appliances, such as an electric iron, use a bimetallic strip thermostat (right). As the iron gets hot, the strip bends and switches off the supply of electricity to the iron. A gas-heated oven uses the type of thermostat shown below. It contains a rod of Invar, which does not expand when heated. The brass tube does expand, closing the valve that controls the flow of gas.

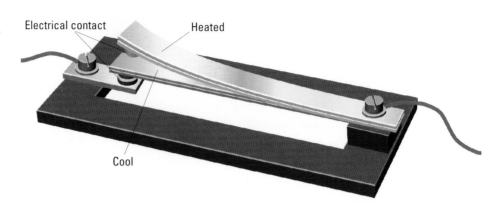

Electrical contact — Heated — Cool

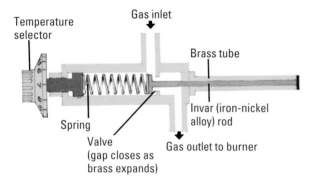

Temperature selector — Gas inlet — Brass tube — Spring — Valve (gap closes as brass expands) — Invar (iron-nickel alloy) rod — Gas outlet to burner

THERMOSTAT (thûr′mə stăt′) A thermostat is a device used to keep the temperature of a system steady (see TEMPERATURE). It works on the principle that certain properties of matter change with temperature. For example, the length of a piece of metal increases with temperature. Different metals increase by different amounts. This effect is used in some thermostats. They contain two metals joined together in a strip called a bimetallic strip (see BIMETALLIC STRIP). When the strip is heated, one of the metals expands, or pushes outward, more than the other (see EXPANSION). This causes the strip to bend. The curving end can be made to operate a switch or a valve, which then turns off the heat supply. In time, the temperature drops. This causes the strip to cool and straighten out. Eventually, the strip straightens out so much that the switch or the valve turns the heat supply on again.

THISTLE (thĭs′əl) Thistles are a group of plants that belong to several genera (plural of *genus*) of the

Thistles grow in temperate regions throughout the world. They have flowers made up of many disk florets and tough stems with spines and prickles.

composite family. Most of them are biennial or perennial herbs. They have tough stems with spines and prickles (see BIENNIAL PLANT; COMPOSITE FAMILY; PERENNIAL PLANT; THORN, SPINE, AND PRICKLE). The rounded flowerhead is made up of many purple disk florets. Each flowerhead turns into a large cluster of fluffy seeds (see FLOWER).

Thistles grow in temperate areas throughout the world. In many places, they are thought of as weeds. Russian thistle, or tumbleweed, is a troublesome weed in many parts of North America. It is not a true thistle, however, because it is a member of the goosefoot family.

See also GOOSEFOOT FAMILY; WEED.

THOMSON, SIR JOSEPH JOHN

(1856–1940) Joseph John Thomson was a British physicist who discovered the electron. The electron is a subatomic particle (a particle that is smaller than an atom) (see ATOM; ELECTRON).

Thomson was born at Cheetham, near Manchester, England, and studied engineering at Owens College (now part of the University of Manchester). Later, he studied physics at Trinity College in Cambridge, where he remained for the rest of his life except for short visits to lecture at Princeton University in New Jersey in 1896 and Yale University in Connecticut in 1904. In 1884, Thomson became Cavendish Professor of Experimental Physics at Cambridge. He held this post until his death. Thomson was awarded the Nobel Prize for physics in 1906.

Thomson's most important research concerned the cathode rays that carried electricity through vacuums. He was able to show that these rays consisted of negatively charged particles that were much smaller than the lightest atoms known. He announced his discovery in 1897. The Dutch physicist Hendrik Lorentz later called the particles electrons. In 1898, Thomson suggested that atoms were made up of negative electrons embedded in a mass of positive material. Later, British physicist Ernest Rutherford proposed that the electrons in an atom moved around a central positive core, or nucleus (see NUCLEUS; RUTHERFORD, ERNEST).

THORAX (thôr′ăks′) The thorax is the part of an animal's body between its head and its abdomen. In insects, the thorax is the middle of three distinct body sections, or parts. The thorax itself is divided into three segments, each of which has a pair of legs. In many insects, the second and third segments

THORAX

The thorax is the part of an animal's body between its head and abdomen. In insects, such as this dragonfly, legs and wings are attached at the thorax.

also carry wings. In some arthropods, such as arachnids and crustaceans, the head and thorax are fused together to form a cephalothorax (see ARTHROPODA; INSECT).

Among the air-breathing vertebrates (animals with backbones), the thorax is the part of the body containing the lungs and the heart. It is also called the chest. It is enclosed by the spine in the back, the sternum, or breastbone, in front, and the ribs on the sides. In mammals, a large sheet of muscle called the diaphragm separates the chest from the abdomen (see DIAPHRAGM; MAMMAL).

See also ABDOMEN; ANATOMY.

THORN, SPINE, AND PRICKLE

Thorns, spines, and prickles are certain parts of plants that are usually sharp, short, and hard. They evolved mainly as a protection against plant-eating animals (see ADAPTATION). Thorns, such as those of the hawthorn tree, are modified stems or twigs. Spines, such as those of cacti (plural of *cactus*), are modified leaves. Prickles, such as those of rose bushes, are modified outgrowths from the surface

THORN, SPINE, AND PRICKLE
The sharp thorns found on some plants are modified stems or twigs. Scientists believe that the thorns, spines, and prickles evolved to protect the plants from being eaten by animals. Pictured are gorse (top) and prickly pear cactus (bottom).

of stems. They are usually curved and their main job is to help the plants to climb.
See also CACTUS FAMILY; HAWTHORN; LEAF; ROSE FAMILY; STEM.

THRASHER A thrasher is a bird that belongs to the family Mimidae. The thrasher copies the songs of other birds. However, the thrasher is not as skillful as its relative, the mockingbird (see MOCKING-BIRD).

There are eight species of thrashers found in North America. In the United States, all of the species except the brown thrasher live in the west and southwest. The brown thrasher lives in the east. A thrasher is about 10 in. [25 cm] long and has a very long brown tail and a long, curved beak. The back and wings of the thrasher are brown, and the breast is either grayish brown or white with brown streaks.
See also BIRD.

THRIPS A thrips is a tiny insect that belongs to the order Thysanoptera. The body of a thrips is from 0.02 to 0.5 in. [0.6 to 13 mm] long and ranges in color from yellow to red to black. Most species have four narrow wings that are fringed with hairs. Thrips reproduce quickly and may produce as many as twelve generations a year in warm climates. In some species, the eggs develop without being fertilized (see PARTHENOGENESIS).

Thrips live on plants in many parts of the world. They are especially common in flowers. Most thrips damage plants by sucking their juices, and some species damage crops. They can also spread disease. As they move from plant to plant, however, thrips do help pollinate flowers. Some species feed on fungi and mites and other small insects.
See also INSECT; POLLINATION.

THRUSH Thrushes are medium-sized birds, generally from 6 to 8 in. [15 to 20 cm] long, belonging to the family Turdidae. Most thrushes are dull brown, but the family contains several colorful North American species, including the robin, the bluebird, and the bluethroat (see BIRD; BLUE-BIRD; ROBIN). Many thrushes have fine songs. Most of them eat fruits, insects, and worms.

THRUSH
The song thrush is known for its habit of eating snails, which it bangs on a rock to break their shells.

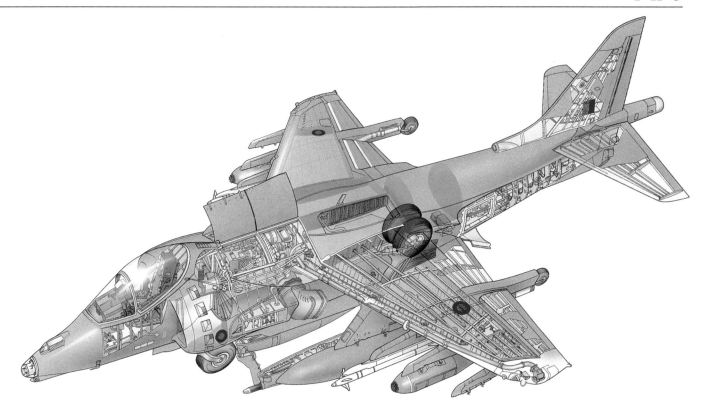

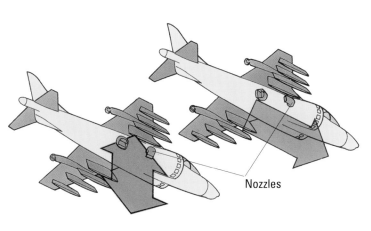

Nozzles

THRUST

The *Harrier* "jump jet" has nozzles that can be rotated to change the direction of the thrust from its powerful turbofan engine. With the nozzles pointing downward, the thrust allows the airplane to take off or land vertically, and even to hover (stay motionless in the air). With the nozzles pointing to the rear, the airplane flies forward like a regular jet.

THRUST Thrust is the forward force produced by powerful engines, such as a jet engine or a rocket. A jet-propelled engine shoots out gases in its exhaust. As the gases are shot out, a force, called a reaction, is produced (see REACTION, PRINCIPLE OF). This reaction pushes the engine forward. The force with which the engine is pushed forward is called the thrust. It is measured in such units of force as newtons (see NEWTON). Modern rocket engines can produce huge thrust forces. For example, the Saturn moon rocket produced a thrust at liftoff of 31 million newtons.

THUNDERSTORM A thunderstorm is a small-scale storm that produces lightning and thunder. Thunderstorms often occur on warm summer afternoons as a result of cold fronts. They can also be caused by cyclones (see COLD FRONT; CYCLONE; LIGHTNING).

Along a cold front, an advancing mass of cold air overtakes a mass of warm air. The warm air is pushed upward until it reaches a height where its moisture condenses (see CONDENSATION). The moisture forms a puffy white cumulus cloud (see CLOUD). Eventually, the cloud develops into a cumulonimbus cloud. A cumulonimbus cloud towers high into the sky, with its upper portion often becoming flattened like an anvil. A cumulonimbus cloud is also called a thunderhead. A strong updraft of air that draws air up into the cloud helps the thunderhead form. A thunderstorm has downdrafts as well as

Thunderstorms often develop on summer afternoons when cold fronts come in. The cold air overtakes a mass of warm air. The warm air is pushed upward until it reaches a height where its moisture condenses into storm clouds.

updrafts. The downdrafts produce the cool wind that often goes ahead of a thunderstorm. When the moisture in the storm leaves the updrafts, it is free to fall to the ground as heavy rain and even hail (see HAIL; RAIN).

The cumulonimbus clouds of a thunderstorm are highly charged with electricity. If the thunderhead comes close enough to a body of opposite electric charge, such as the earth's surface, a visible spark, or lightning, results. When lightning travels through the atmosphere, it heats up the air around it. The heated air expands, thus compressing the colder air. This causes air waves that have the sound of thunder.
See also WEATHER.

TIBIA (tĭb′ē ə) The tibia is the second longest bone in the human body. The femur is the only bone that is longer. The tibia is the innermost of the two bones in the lower leg of humans and other vertebrates (animals with backbones). The other bone in the lower leg is the fibula (see BONE; FEMUR; FIBULA).

The tibia runs along the front of the leg. At its top end, the tibia forms the bottom half of the knee joint. At its bottom end, the tibia forms the bulge

at the inside of the ankle. The tibia is also called the shinbone.
See also SKELETON.

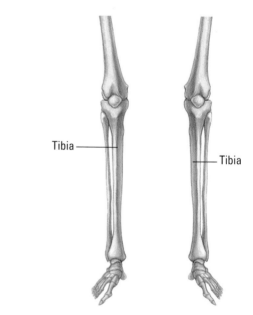

Tibia

Tibia

TIBIA

The tibia, or shinbone, is the largest of the two bones in the lower leg. Its ends form parts of the knee and ankle joints.

TICK Ticks are small, parasitic animals that belong to the order Acarina. They are arachnids, not insects (see ARACHNID; INSECT; PARASITE). Ticks have oval bodies and eight legs that stick out

TICK
Ticks are small, parasitic arachnids that attack various hosts, including human beings.

like those of a crab. A tick's head is small and can move only a little. It has weak eyes and no antennae (see ANTENNAE). Its beak is sharp and barbed to keep it firmly in the skin of its host. The tick jabs its beak into a host—usually a mammal, bird, or reptile—and sucks blood until the tick has swelled to many times its normal size. It then drops off and digests its meal. A tick knows when a possible victim approaches because of the carbon dioxide the animal breathes out.

After mating, a tick lays thousands of eggs on the ground, not on a host. These eggs develop into six-legged larvae. Each larva (singular of *larvae*) climbs blades of grass and waits for a host to pass by to which it can attach itself. After sucking blood from the host, the larva molts—sheds it outer covering—and becomes an eight-legged nymph (see MOLTING). After sucking more blood, the nymph molts and becomes an adult. Some ticks go through this metamorphosis, or change, on one host. Most species, though, require several hosts, dropping off before each molt (see METAMORPHOSIS).

Most ticks attack many different kinds of hosts, including human beings. Many ticks are dangerous because they carry and spread diseases. Some ticks can inject a poison that paralyzes victims. However, these ticks are rare. In the United States, two species of ticks, the Rocky Mountain wood tick and the American dog tick, spread the disease known as Rocky Mountain spotted fever (see RICKETTSIA). Outbreaks of this dangerous, and sometimes fatal, disease are reported every year. Some cases occur in the Rocky Mountains, but most are in the southeastern coastal areas. A small tick called a deer tick may carry a bacterium that can cause a serious disease in humans. This disease, called Lyme arthritis or Lyme disease, may be treated with antibiotics (see ANTIBIOTIC; ARTHRITIS; BACTERIA).

Once a tick has attached itself to the skin, it is very difficult to remove. If it is pulled off, the beak usually remains in the skin and may cause an infected sore. The best way to remove a tick is to cover it with petroleum jelly or a heavy oil. It then releases its hold and can be removed.

TIDE The tide is the regular rise and fall of ocean waters. Tides are caused by the gravitational pull of the moon and sun on the earth's ocean (see EARTH; GRAVITY; MOON; SUN). All bodies of water are influenced by the moon and sun. However, it is only where oceans and continents meet that tides are noticeable.

The moon's gravity pulls the water on the side of the earth nearest the moon. This causes the water level to rise, and is called a tidal bulge. At the same time, on the opposite side of the earth, the solid earth is closer to the moon than the water is. The moon's gravity pulls the solid earth away from the water. This causes a second tidal

TIDE
At low tide (top), the beach is exposed. As the tide comes in (bottom), rocks and sand that were visible at low tide are covered by the water.

bulge. These two bulges are where high tides occur.

As the earth rotates on its axis, the land and water rotate together. The tidal bulges, however, always stay in the same position—one nearest the moon, and the other on the opposite side of the earth. Because the earth completes a rotation every 24 hours, each part of the ocean passes under both tidal bulges every day. This means that each part of the ocean has two high tides daily. The time between high tides is about 12 hours and 25 minutes. This time period is regulated by the rotation of the earth and the revolution of the moon.

Once the water reaches high tide, it falls for about six hours until it reaches its lowest position, called low tide. Then the cycle begins again. The difference in water level between high tide and low tide is called the tidal range. Some locations along the coast have much greater ranges than others. For example, the Bay of Fundy on Canada's Atlantic Ocean coast has a tidal range of about 50 ft. [15 m]. Other places, such as the Mediterranean Sea, have a very small range. Unusually high tides, called spring tides, occur when the earth, moon, and sun are in a straight line. Spring tides occur during the full and new phases of the moon. When the sun, earth, and moon form a right angle, the lowest, or neap, tides occur. Neap tides occur when the moon is in its first and third quarters (see NEAP TIDE).

Tides help humans. For example, hydroelectric power can be produced by incoming and outgoing tides.

See also HYDROELECTRIC POWER.

TIGER The tiger is the largest of all cats (see CAT). Wild tigers are found only in Asia. Tigers can live in almost any climate from the cold wastes of Siberia to the steaming jungles of Malaysia. They need only shade, water, and prey (see PREDATORS AND PREY).

The tiger's coat ranges from orange red to brownish yellow and is marked with black stripes. These stripes vary in length, width, and spacing. Many tigers have a fringe of hair around the sides of the head. The darkest tigers live in the tropical forests.

Adult male tigers may grow to 9 ft. [2.7 m] in length. This length includes the tail, which is about 3 ft. [0.9 m] long. The males weigh about 420 lb. [191 kg]. The females, called tigresses, may grow to 8 ft. [2.4 m] in length, including the tail. They weigh about 300 lb. [136 kg]. The biggest tigers are Siberian tigers. The gestation period of a tigress ranges from about 95 to 105 days (see GESTATION PERIOD). A litter usually consists of two or three baby tigers, called cubs.

Tigers prefer to feed on large prey, such as antelope, deer, and wild pigs. Tigers hunt at night. They depend mainly on their sharp eyes and keen ears.

The number of tigers has been greatly reduced. The animals have been widely hunted by humans. In addition, many of the forests in which they once lived have been cleared for development. The tiger is an endangered species. Only a few thousand animals are left. The tiger will become extinct unless it is completely protected.

See also ENDANGERED SPECIES; EXTINCTION.

TIGER

The tiger is the largest of all cats. Wild tigers are found only in Asia. Tigers are considered an endangered species and will become extinct unless they are completely protected.

Time is the system used by humans to measure periods between events. Through the ages, humans have based the measurement of time on many different factors. These factors include the rotation (spin) of the earth, the movements of the moon and stars, and the changing of the seasons. Perhaps the earliest measurement of time was based on the regular cycle of night and day. This cycle is caused by the rotation of the earth on its axis (an imaginary line running through the center of the earth, from pole to pole). The time it takes the earth to make one complete turn on its axis is called the solar day. The length of the solar day varies according to location and season. The twenty-four-hour period between one midnight and the next is called the mean solar day (see EARTH). Time is also measured by the earth's rotation with respect to the stars. This type of time measurement is called sidereal time. Astronomers, who need a highly accurate measurement of time, use sidereal time.

Animals and plants have natural time cycles. Diurnal rhythms are the natural biological cycles that recur daily in most animals and plants (see BIORHYTHMS). Geological time traces the history of the earth back several billion years. Scientists use complex methods of dating to find the age of ancient rocks and fossils (see DATING; FOSSIL; GEOLOGICAL TIME SCALE).

Humans have continually tried to find more accurate methods of measuring time. In 1970, there was a difference of 26.3 seconds between calendar time and solar time. This difference will increase by 0.53 seconds every century because of slight changes in the earth's movements. For some scientific purposes that require very accurate time standards, the time that is based on heavenly bodies is too inaccurate. The most accurate way of measuring time is by an atomic clock. An atomic clock measures the vibrations of certain atoms. Atomic clocks are accurate to within millionths of a second per year. The world changed to atomic time at the beginning of 1972.

See also CALENDAR; CLOCK AND WATCH; TIME ZONE.

TIMEKEEPING DEVICES

Early timekeeping devices included the candle clock, hourglass, and sundial. The first mechanical clocks were invented in the 1300s. After Galileo discovered the principle of the pendulum in 1538, the pendulum clock was developed.

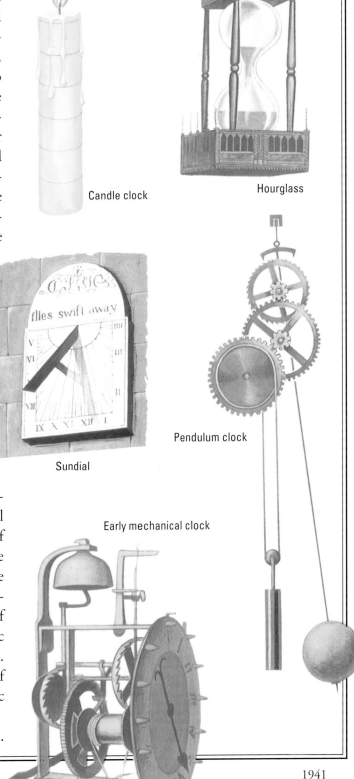

Candle clock

Hourglass

Sundial

Pendulum clock

Early mechanical clock

TIME ZONE A time zone is one of twenty-four regions into which the earth is divided as part of the standard time system. Each time zone differs by one hour from the divisions that are before and after it. The earth rotates on its axis (an imaginary line running through the center of the earth, from pole to pole) a full 360° every twenty-four hours, or 15° every hour. Thus, by international agreement, the earth has been divided into twenty-four time zones, each differing by 15°, or one hour.

Because of certain boundaries, such as those of countries, the divisions between time zones do not always run along lines of longitude, or meridians (see LATITUDE AND LONGITUDE). The meridian that runs through Greenwich, England, is considered 0° longitude. It is called the prime meridian. The international date line is 180° east or west of the prime meridian. The area east of the international date line is one day earlier than the area west of it. This means that a traveler crossing the international date line going east gains one day. A traveler crossing the international date line going west loses one day (see INTERNATIONAL DATE LINE; PRIME MERIDIAN).

Large countries, such as the United States, are divided into several time zones. Except for Alaska and Hawaii, the United States is split into four time zones: Eastern, Central, Mountain, and Pacific. *See also* STANDARD TIME.

TIME ZONE

In general, time zones are centered on meridians, with one time zone covering about 15° longitude. However, national borders and other considerations have resulted in time zones being somewhat irregular. Each color on the map is a different time zone. Blue areas indicate zones in which the time differs from the time in an adjoining zone by half an hour rather than one hour.

TIN Tin (Sn) is a silvery white metallic element. The main ore of tin is the mineral cassiterite. This ore is found in many parts of the world. The tin is easily taken out by heating the ore. Tin has been known since ancient times (see ELEMENT; ORE).

Tin's atomic number is 50, and its relative atomic mass is 118.69. Tin exists in two different

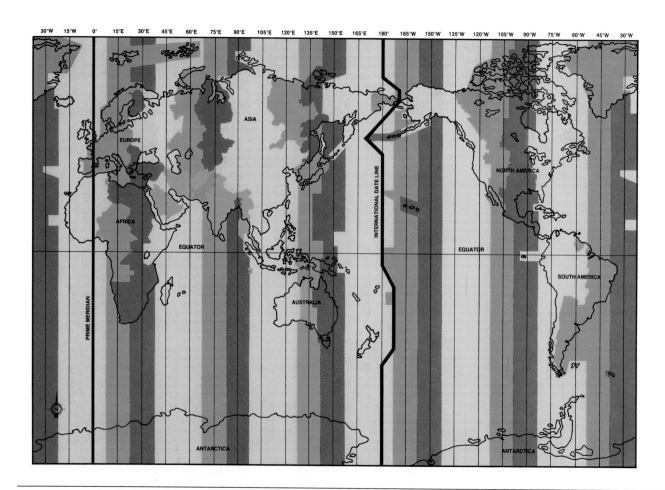

TIN

Tin has a variety of uses. An important compound of tin, stannic chloride, is used in the tanning and dyeing processes to make animal hide into leather used to make clothing (above). Tin's main use is as a corrosion-resistant coating on steel for food and drink cans (below), some of which are fitted with an aluminum ring-pull tab.

forms. These different forms are called allotropes. The normal form is the silvery metal that is known as white tin. At temperatures below 55°F [13°C], white tin slowly changes into a gray powder called gray tin. Gray tin is denser than white tin.

Tin is resistant to corrosion (see CORROSION). Because of this property, it is used in tin cans. Tin cans are actually made of steel with a coating of tin. Another important use for tin is in alloys (see ALLOY). Important tin alloys include bronze and pewter (see BRONZE; PEWTER).

Tin forms two series of compounds. They are called tin (II), or stannous, compounds and tin (IV), or stannic, compounds. The mineral cassiterite is stannic oxide (SnO_2). One of the most important compounds of tin is stannic chloride ($SnCl_4$). It is used in dyeing and tanning (making animal hide into leather). Tin compounds may be sprayed onto glass to produce a coating that can conduct electricity. Such coatings can be used for frost-free windshields.

Tin's density is 7.3 grams per cubic centimeter. The difference between the melting point of tin, 482°F [250°C], and its boiling point, 4,717°F [2,603°C], is one of the widest of any metal.

See also COMPOUND.

TISSUE

A tissue is a group of cells, all more or less alike, that work together to do certain things in an organism (see CELL). Some tissues are called simple tissues because they do only one thing. Other tissues are called composite tissues because they do several things. Different tissues with related tasks may be grouped together to form an organ, such as the heart or liver (see ORGAN). One-celled organisms do many of the same things that the tissues of multicellular organisms do. One-celled organisms, however, have no tissues.

Animal tissues Animal tissues are classified in many ways. The most useful way to classify them is by the task they perform. Animal tissues have five basic tasks: energy production, coordination, support and movement, reproduction, and blood cell production.

Animals use food and oxygen to produce energy. Many tissues are needed to digest and absorb food, carry it throughout the body, excrete wastes, and exchange and carry gases. These tissues form the digestive, circulatory, excretory, and respiratory systems (see CIRCULATORY SYSTEM; DIGESTIVE SYSTEM; EXCRETION; RESPIRATORY SYSTEM). Most of the tissues in these systems are made of epithelial cells (see BLOOD; EPITHELIUM).

Coordination tissues control the way certain internal and external parts of the body work together. Coordination tissues make up the nervous and the endocrine systems. The nervous system includes the brain, spinal cord, and nerves (see NERVOUS SYSTEM). The sense organs, such as the eyes, are closely related to the nervous system. The endocrine system includes all the glands that produce hormones (see ENDOCRINE; HORMONE).

Support and movement tissues include bones, cartilage, connective tissue, muscles, and skin (see BONE; CARTILAGE; CONNECTIVE TISSUE; MUSCLE; SKIN). They make up the integumentary (skin), muscular, and skeletal systems (see SKELETON).

Reproductive tissues make up the essential part of the reproductive system. They produce the gametes, or sex cells—the sperm in the male and the eggs in the female (see REPRODUCTIVE SYSTEM).

The blood-producing tissues produce the red blood cells, white blood cells, and platelets. In some vertebrates (animals with a backbone), these tissues are located in the spleen. In mammals, however, blood cells are produced mostly in bone marrow (see SPLEEN).

There are several important body fluids that are closely related to the tissues. Lymph is a colorless, watery liquid that passes through body tissues carrying dissolved substances in it (see LYMPH).

ANIMAL TISSUE
Animal brains, including the human brain (right), are made up of coordination tissues. These tissues control the way certain internal and external parts of the body work together.

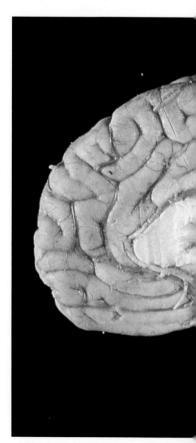

CELLS
All tissues are made up of a collection of similar cells. Shown at left are nerve cells in the human brain.

PLANT TISSUE

The microscope photograph (right) shows a close-up of a leaf. The oval structures are small pores (called stomata) that allow carbon dioxide from the air to enter the tissues of the leaf. The carbon dioxide then takes part in photosynthesis.

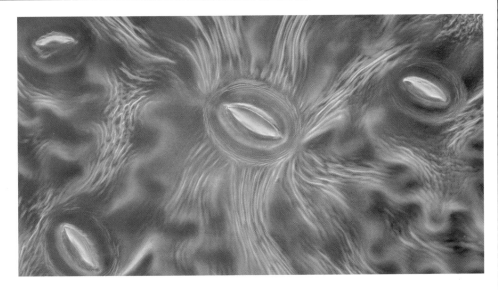

Plant tissues All plant tissues start out as meristem (see MERISTEM). They are classified by task and location. The three main types of plant tissues are dermal, vascular, and fundamental.

Dermal tissues protect a plant and limit the amount of water lost through transpiration (see TRANSPIRATION). They also control gas exchange. There are two kinds of dermal tissue: epidermis and, in woody plants, periderm. Epidermis covers the outer surface of all the structures of a plant. It produces a

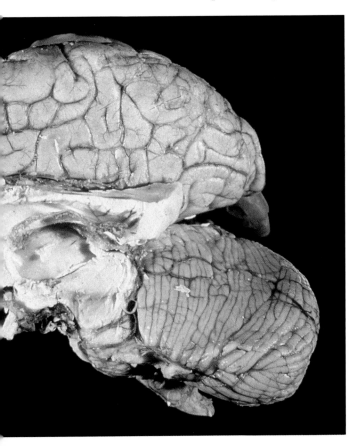

waxy substance called cutin. In many plants, cutin forms an extra layer outside of the epidermis. The epidermis also has such structures as stomata (plural of *stoma*), glands, and hairlike outgrowths, including root hairs (see STOMA). In most woody plants, periderm acts like an internal epidermis. It is produced by the cambium and is made up of cork cells (see BARK; CAMBIUM; CORK; WOODY PLANT).

Vascular tissues are the transporting structures found in most higher plants (see VASCULAR PLANT). There are two types of vascular tissue: xylem and phloem. Xylem is made up of cells that transport water and dissolved minerals upward from the roots (see XYLEM). Phloem transports dissolved food from the leaves to all other parts of the plant (see PHLOEM).

Fundamental tissue makes up the bulk of most plants. There are four types: parenchyma, collenchyma, sclerenchyma, and endodermis. Parenchyma is the most common tissue in vascular plants. It makes up the cortex, pith, fruit pulp, and part of the leaf. It is also associated with the vascular tissues. Collenchyma is supportive tissue (see COLLENCHYMA). It is found in stems and leaves. Sclerenchyma is also supportive tissue (see SCLERENCHYMA). It is made of cells that have lost their protoplasm. The endodermis is a layer of cells that encloses the vascular tissue, separating it from the surrounding cortex (see CORTEX). Its function is uncertain.

See also ANIMAL KINGDOM; DIFFERENTIATION, CELLULAR; HISTOLOGY; PLANT KINGDOM.

TITANIUM
Titanium is a strong, corrosion-resistant metal. Titanium alloys are used to make aircraft and jet engines.

TITANIUM (tī tā′nē əm) Titanium (Ti) is a white metallic element (see ELEMENT). The English chemist William Gregor discovered titanium in 1791. It is one of the most common of all metals and occurs in the minerals rutile and ilmenite (see MINERAL). Titanium is taken from these minerals by a very costly process. Therefore, though it is common, it is an expensive metal. Titanium is a very light metal, but it is also strong. It resists corrosion and the action of chemicals (see CORROSION). These qualities make titanium a very useful metal in alloys (see ALLOY). Titanium alloys are used in aircraft and in jet engines. Titanium is particularly resistant to salt water and is used in underwater parts of ships, such as propellers. It is also used in surgery for joining fractured bones.

The most important compound of titanium is titanium dioxide (TiO_2). It is a brilliant white pigment (coloring substance) used in paints. The mineral rutile consists of titanium dioxide. Titanium forms an acid called titanic acid (H_2TiO_4). Titanic acid is used in dyeing (see ACID).

Titanium's atomic number is 22, and its relative atomic mass is 47.9. It melts at about 3,033°F [1,667°C] and boils at 5,949°F [3,287°C]. Its relative density is 4.5.
See also RELATIVE DENSITY.

TITMOUSE (tĭt′mous′) A titmouse is a small bird that belongs to the family Paridae. There are sixty-two species found throughout the world, except in South America, Australia, Indonesia, and islands of the South Pacific. Four species live in North America and range from 4 to 5 in. [11 to 13 cm] in length. Their bodies are gray above and white below. All titmice have a tuft, or crest, of feathers on top of the head. Titmice eat insects and seeds found in the woodlands.
See also BIRD.

TITMOUSE—**American species**
The verdin (left) is a member of the titmouse family from western North America. Other titmice are known as chickadees.

TITMOUSE—**Asian species**
The Chinese yellow tit is a small bird with striking yellow and black coloration.

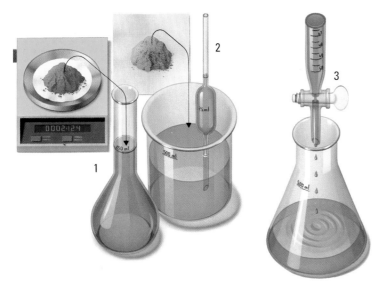

TITRATION
(1) To perform a titration, a chemist first weighs a sample of a substance and then dissolves it in an exact volume of solution. This is called the standard solution. (2) An unweighed sample of a second substance is dissolved in water. A known volume of it is then removed using a pipette. (3) Finally, the standard solution is added from a burette until the reaction is complete—usually detected by an indicator.

TITRATION (tī trā′shən) Titration is a method of analysis used in chemistry. It enables the chemist to find the concentration of a solution (see SOLUTION AND SOLUBILITY). A measured amount of the solution with the unknown concentration is placed in a flask using a device called a pipette (see PIPETTE). A flask is a glass bottle with a narrow neck and wide bottom. Then, another solution is placed in a burette. A burette is a glass tube that is marked with a scale and has a faucet at the bottom. The concentration of this second solution is known. The second solution is added to the flask containing the first solution so the two react. The chemist reads the scale on the burette to tell how much of the second solution has been added. A substance called an indicator is used to tell the chemist when all of the solution in the flask has reacted (see INDICATOR). In some cases, the chemist may use electrical instruments instead of an indicator. The chemist knows the amounts of the two solutions and also the concentration of the solution in the burette. The chemist can then calculate the concentration of the first solution.
See also CHEMICAL ANALYSIS.

TNT TNT is an explosive compound (see COMPOUND). The letters stand for trinitrotoluene (trī nī′trō tŏl′yoo ēn′). Its formula is $CH_3C_6H_2(NO_2)_3$. It is made from toluene ($C_6H_5CH_3$) (see TOLUENE). The toluene is reacted with a mixture of nitric and sulfuric acids (see NITRIC ACID; SULFURIC ACID). The reaction is in three stages. At each stage, a nitro group ($-NO_2$) replaces one of the hydrogen atoms in toluene.

TNT forms pale yellow crystals that melt at 176°F [80°C]. TNT was discovered in 1863. However, it was not known to be explosive until later. This was because TNT does not explode when it is heated or struck. TNT has to be exploded by a device called a detonator. The detonator itself explodes and sets off the TNT.
See also EXPLOSIVE.

TOAD A toad is a small froglike animal with long back legs. Toads belong to a group of amphibians called the anurans. There are about three hundred species of toads, and they are found all over the world. Most toads grow up in water as tadpoles but spend the majority of their lives on land (see AMPHIBIAN; FROG).

Toads are similar to frogs, but most have rough warts on their skin. They also have bumplike glands on their skin that contain a poisonous liquid (see GLAND). Toads release this liquid when attacked. Toads average from 2 to 4 in. [5 to 13 cm] in length, but some are much longer.

Most toads have long, sticky tongues that they flick out to catch insects and other small animals for food. Toads mate in or near water during the spring and summer. The male attracts the female with a mating call. It makes the call by filling up a balloonlike part of its throat with air. It then forces

TOAD

Toads generally move slowly on land. They have a waddling walk. When startled, toads can make long leaps. Pictured here are (1) an Eastern spadefoot toad from eastern Europe and southwest Asia; (2) a natterjack toad catching a fly with its long tongue; (3) a female Surinam toad carrying her eggs in the skin on her back; and (4) a painted toad.

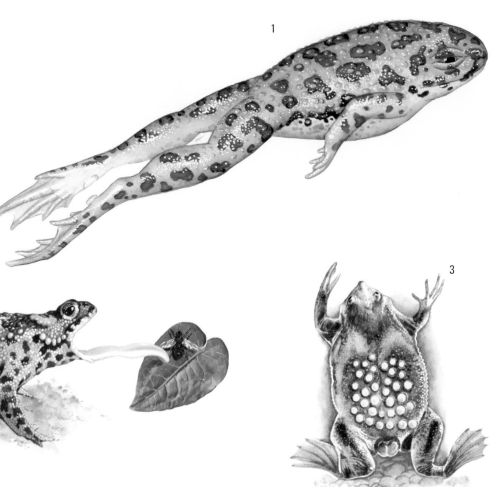

the air across its vocal cords, causing them to vibrate and make a loud noise. Most adult toads make their homes in fields and gardens, but some live in deserts.

TOBACCO (tə băk′ō) Tobacco is an annual plant that belongs to the nightshade family, Solanaceae. Tobacco leaves are used in making cigarettes, cigars, pipe tobacco, and chewing tobacco (see ANNUAL PLANT; NIGHTSHADE FAMILY).

The use of tobacco for smoking probably began with Native Americans, who used it long before Christopher Columbus arrived in the Americas in 1492 (see SMOKING). Columbus brought some of the tobacco seeds back to Europe, and farmers began to grow tobacco there. Pipe smoking soon became popular. Hand-rolled cigarettes appeared in Spain around 1600. Cigarettes did not become popular in the United States until the 1850s.

Today, tobacco is an important crop in more than sixty countries. In the United States alone, farmers harvest about 2 billion lb. [0.9 billion kg] of tobacco leaves each year. North Carolina is the leading tobacco-producing state. Kentucky, South Carolina, and Tennessee are other states that produce large crops. The annual value of tobacco products in the United States amounts to over $17 billion.

TOBACCO
Tobacco is an important cash crop in many countries. In the United States alone, tobacco products are worth more than $17 billion each year.

Smoking became an important topic of discussion in the United States in the 1960s and 1970s. Many doctors warned that the substances called tars that are produced by burning tobacco are a main cause of lung cancer (see CANCER). Also, doctors have warned about the nicotine found in tobacco products. Nicotine is a stimulant that works on the heart, nervous system, and other organs (see STIMULANT). Heavy amounts of nicotine are poisonous to the human body. Many physicians believe that nicotine helps bring about heart attacks and stomach ulcers.

In answer to these warnings from doctors, most cigarette manufacturers have reduced the tar and nicotine content of their products. However, doctors still warn that these measures have not eliminated the dangers of smoking. In 1964, the United States government declared that all cigarette packages must carry a health warning. This warning, which must also appear in advertising, was strengthened in 1969 and again in 1984. Most states today have restrictions regarding smoking in public places, because increasing evidence indicates that nonsmokers also may be harmed by smoke.

The tobacco plant grows to a height of 4 to 6 ft. [1.2 to 1.8 m]. It produces about twenty leaves. Each leaf is up to 30 in. [76 cm] long and 15 to 18 in. [38 to 46 cm] wide. The leaves range from light green to dark green.

To make the tobacco used in tobacco products, the leaves have to be cured, or dried. Curing dries the sap from the leaves (see SAP). The most widely used method of curing is called flue curing. In flue curing, heat from flues (pipes) that are connected to furnaces dry the leaves. The process takes about a week. When cured, tobacco turns yellowish brown to dark brown.

TOLUENE (tŏl′yoō ēn′) Toluene ($C_6H_5CH_3$) is a colorless, flammable liquid. It boils at 232°F [111°C]. Toluene is a hydrocarbon because its molecules contain only atoms of hydrogen and carbon (see HYDROCARBON). A molecule of toluene contains a benzene ring (C_6H_6) with a methyl group (-CH_3) replacing one of the hydrogen atoms. Because it contains a benzene ring, toluene is known as an aromatic hydrocarbon. Toluene is obtained from coal and petroleum (see BENZENE; COAL; PETROLEUM). It is used to make a wide range of substances such as TNT, phenols, dyes, and perfumes (see PHENOL; TNT). Toluene is also a very important solvent (substance that dissolves other substances) in industry (see SOLVENT).

TOMATO The tomato plant is a plant that belongs to the nightshade family, Solanaceae. It grows to a height of about 6 ft. [1.8 m]. It has long, pinnately compound leaves and clusters of small,

TOMATO

Modern tomato plants (above) are cultivated varieties developed from a wild plant that came originally from South America. The fruit (right) is used raw in salads, in cooking, and to make tomato juice.

yellow star-shaped flowers (see LEAF; FLOWER). The tomato plant produces a juicy red berry called a tomato (see BERRY). The tomato is often more than 3 in. [7.5 cm] across, although several small-fruited varieties are cultivated. Tomatoes are rich in vitamins A and C and are a popular food throughout the world. Many people refer to the tomato as a vegetable, but it is really a fruit. It came originally from South America.

See also ANNUAL PLANT; FRUIT; NIGHTSHADE FAMILY; VEGETABLE; VITAMIN.

TOMBAUGH, CLYDE WILLIAM (1906–)

(tŏm' bô, klīd) Clyde Tombaugh is an American astronomer. He was born in Streator, Illinois. Tombaugh began his career as an assistant at Lowell Observatory in Flagstaff, Arizona. He was helping other astronomers who were searching for a planet beyond Neptune (see NEPTUNE). American astronomer Percival Lowell had predicted that such a planet would be found (see LOWELL, PERCIVAL). After a year's work comparing photographs of the part of the sky where Lowell had expected to find the planet, Tombaugh found it. He saw from the photographs, which had been taken every three days, that a faint "star" had moved. After careful observation of this body for a month, it was determined to be a planet. The discovery of this planet, Pluto, was announced on March 13, 1930.

See also ASTRONOMY; PLUTO.

TOMOGRAPHY

Tomography is a way of creating a precise image of a selected "slice," or plane, inside the human body. It is usually done using a machine called a computerized tomography (CT) scanner, which is a ring-shaped X-ray machine (see COMPUTED TOMOGRAPHY; X RAY). The patient lies inside the ring, and the scanner is rotated through 180 degrees. As it rotates, it takes many X-ray measurements every few degrees. Although many pictures are taken during the process, the patient is exposed to a much lower dose of radiation than he or she would receive in a normal X-ray examination.

The huge amount of information collected using the CT scanner is processed by a computer to provide a series of pictures of the inside of the patient's body. The individual slices can also be combined to form a three-dimensional image. Tomography is a very useful tool to allow doctors to see inside a patient's body and to help them find out what is wrong.

See also RADIOGRAPHY.

TONGUE

In vertebrates (animals with a backbone), the tongue is a muscular organ in the mouth, although not all vertebrates have a tongue (see VERTEBRATE). In most species, the tongue is the chief organ of the sense of taste (see TASTE AND SMELL). It is usually attached at the rear of the mouth, but in some frogs and toads, it is fixed at the front and is flicked out to catch food. Several other animals use their tongues to collect food. Anteaters, for example, have a long sticky tongue with which they sweep up ants and termites (see ANTEATER). Woodpeckers also have a long tongue with which they probe for insects in tree trunks (see WOODPECKER). Snakes and lizards use their tongues to gather scent particles from their surroundings (see LIZARD; SNAKE). Many mammals use their tongues to help them swallow food (see MAMMAL).

TONGUE

A Bengal tiger licks its lips to clean the fur around its mouth after a meal.

The human tongue is important in articulation, which is the formation of different sounds during speech (see SOUND; VOICE).

Butterflies and moths suck nectar and other liquids with a slender tube called a proboscis (see BUTTERFLY AND MOTH). It is often called a tongue, but it is very different from the vertebrate tongue. It is made from small structures around the mouth, and is not actually inside the mouth.

TONSIL (tŏn′səl) The tonsils are masses of tissue located at the back of the mouth of humans and other mammals (see MAMMAL; TISSUE). They are made of the same kind of tissue as lymph nodes and seem to have a role in protecting the body from infection (see INFECTION; LYMPHATIC SYSTEM). The tonsils are covered with thin layers of connective tissue and mucous membrane (see CONNECTIVE TISSUE; MUCOUS MEMBRANE).

There are three pairs of tonsils: palatine, pharyngeal, and lingual. The palatine tonsils can be easily seen on each side of the throat. The palatine tonsils usually become smaller as a person grows older. The pharyngeal tonsils, or adenoids, are in the back of the nasal passages leading to the throat (see ADENOIDS). They also became smaller with age. The lingual tonsils are at the base of the tongue.

Tonsillitis is a painful swelling of the tonsils, usually the palatine tonsils. It is caused by certain bacteria or viruses (see BACTERIA; VIRUS). Its symptoms are a sore throat, fever, difficulty in swallowing, and swelling in the neck. If the disease becomes severe, it may spread to other parts of the body. It may eventually damage the heart, lungs, or kidneys. If the tonsils become infected repeatedly, they may be removed in a surgical operation known as tonsillectomy.

TOPAZ (tō′păz′) Topaz is a very hard mineral with a rating of eight on the Mohs scale (see HARDNESS; MINERAL). Topaz is a compound of aluminum, silicon, oxygen, and fluorine (see ALUMINUM; COMPOUND; FLUORINE; OXYGEN; SILICON). Most topaz is not gem quality and occurs as gray white masses, which are easily confused with quartz (see PRECIOUS STONE AND GEM; QUARTZ). Transparent gem-quality crystals of topaz may be blue, green, pink, white, or yellow. The most prized gem topaz is light brown, pinkish red, or golden yellow.

Topaz is mined chiefly in Brazil, the former Soviet Union, and the United States. Brazil is the major producer of precious topaz.

TOPAZ

Topaz is one of the earth's hardest minerals. Most gem-quality topaz comes from Brazil.

TOPOLOGY

Topology (tə pŏl′ə jē) is a part of geometry (see GEOMETRY). Unlike most geometry, however, topology has nothing to do with measurements. It has to do with the effects of stretching and bending different shapes without cutting them. Imagine a sphere made of a soft material that can be changed into a cube by simply molding it. No cutting is needed. This means that both these shapes are topologically equivalent to any other shape that does not have a hole in it.

A shape that is not topologically equivalent to a sphere is a torus, which is shaped like a doughnut. This is because a hole has to be cut into a sphere to make it a torus. The torus is topologically equivalent to a coffee cup. This is because both shapes contain one hole. A torus can be changed into a coffee cup.

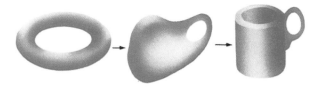

Topology has to do with surfaces. One surface that topologists have invented is called a Mobius band or Mobius strip. A Mobius band can be made by taking a strip of paper and giving it a half twist. The two ends are then joined together. If a line is drawn along a Mobius band, its two ends will always meet. Also, the line will appear on both sides of the band.

There is an interesting problem in topology called the four-color problem. Suppose you wanted to color a map so that no two countries with a common boundary have the same color. Only four colors are needed for the map—no matter what the shape of the countries. A map has never been drawn that needed a fifth color. The problem was that topologists had difficulty proving that this was true. They began working on this problem in the 1800s. It has been proved only recently.

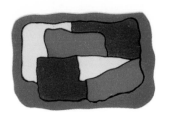

Another part of topology has to do with networks. A network is any set of lines that join points. The points are known as nodes and the lines as arcs. The areas inside the lines are called regions. There are different kinds of networks. A traversable network is one that can be traced without lifting the pen from the drawing. Also, the pen does not go over any line twice (see below left). The same cannot be said for a network that is not traversable (see below right). The eighteenth-century Swiss mathematician Leonhard Euler discovered a formula for traversable networks. The number of nodes (N), arcs (A), and regions (R) are connected by this formula: N + R = A + 2. A similar formula is used for polyhedra (plural of *polyhedron*).

See also POLYGON AND POLYHEDRON.

TORNADO

A tornado is a violent windstorm that develops from a large thunderstorm. Tornadoes can do enormous damage and cause great loss of life. Pictured at right is the funnel cloud of a tornado.

TORNADO (tôr nā′dō) A tornado is a strong windstorm that develops from a large thunderstorm (see THUNDERSTORM). Tornadoes usually form along a cold front that separates cool, dry air from warm, humid (moist) air (see COLD FRONT). As the cool, dry air forces the warm, humid air upward, thunderstorms can result. A line of thunderstorms is called a squall line. Some of these thunderstorms may become large enough to develop the type of wind circulation a cyclone has (see CYCLONE). A rotating cloud shaped like a funnel may then come down from the thunderstorm, drawing air up into it. The air, moving around and around on its way up, brings with it dust and debris. When the funnel, or tornado, reaches the surface of the earth, it causes great destruction.

The width of a tornado varies from about 10 ft. to 1 mi. [3 m to 1.6 km]. The winds near the center can be as high as 300 m.p.h. [480 kph]. Tornadoes have a forward speed of about 10 to 25 m.p.h. [16 to 40 kph]. The air pressure inside a tornado is very low. Buildings sometimes explode outward because of the low air pressure around them (see AIR).

Tornadoes can pick up such large objects as automobiles and houses and carry them great distances. Tornadoes occur most often in Australia and the United States. They are found especially in the midwestern and southern United States. Tornadoes that form or cross over water are called waterspouts.

TORQUE (tôrk) A torque is a force that tends to produce a twisting or turning effect. It is also the name given to the turning effect (or moment) of a force (see FORCE; MOMENT). Torque is measured by the force applied multiplied by the perpendicular distance between the force and the point about which the object turns (see FULCRUM). Torque is increased by increasing the force. Torque is also increased by applying the force farther from the

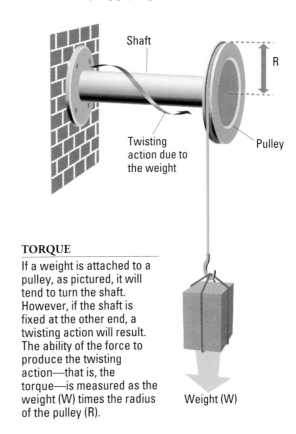

Shaft

R

Twisting action due to the weight

Pulley

TORQUE

If a weight is attached to a pulley, as pictured, it will tend to turn the shaft. However, if the shaft is fixed at the other end, a twisting action will result. The ability of the force to produce the twisting action—that is, the torque—is measured as the weight (W) times the radius of the pulley (R).

Weight (W)

center of the object. For example, if a force is applied to the rim of a wheel, the wheel spins faster than if the force is applied closer to the center of the wheel. Two parallel forces acting in opposite directions may also produce a twisting action. This happens when you roll a pencil between your hands.

TORRICELLI, EVANGELISTA (1608–1647) (tôr ĭ chĕl' ē, ĕ vän' jĕ lē' stä) Evangelista Torricelli was an Italian physicist. He was born in Faenza, Italy, and studied in Rome. He worked for Galileo during the last three months of Galileo's life (see GALILEO).

Before Galileo died, he suggested that Torricelli should do some research into vacuums (see VACUUM). In 1643, while Torricelli was following this advice, he experimented with a tube of mercury (see MERCURY). He filled a tube that was closed at one end with mercury. He turned the tube upside down in a container of mercury. The mercury fell down the tube into the container, leaving what Torricelli correctly thought was a vacuum at the top. However, all the mercury in the tube did not empty into the container. Some remained in the tube. Torricelli noticed that the height of the mercury in the tube was not always the same. It changed from day to day, sometimes going above 30 in. [76.2 cm] and sometimes below. Torricelli determined how atmospheric pressure made the mercury move. He had invented the first barometer, an instrument for measuring air pressure. A unit called the torr, used by scientists to measure gas pressure, is named after him.

See also ATMOSPHERE; BAROMETER; PHYSICS.

TORSION (tôr'shən) Suppose that you have a bar that is fixed at one end. If enough force is applied, the free end can be twisted around. This twisting is called torsion. If the bar is elastic, it tends to resist the twisting (see ELASTICITY). More and more force is needed to twist it further. If the force is removed, the bar unwinds and returns to its first state. Torsion occurs in mobiles that are hung from ceilings. The mobile is continually twisting around because of the air currents in the room. The wire that holds it is always subjected to torsion.

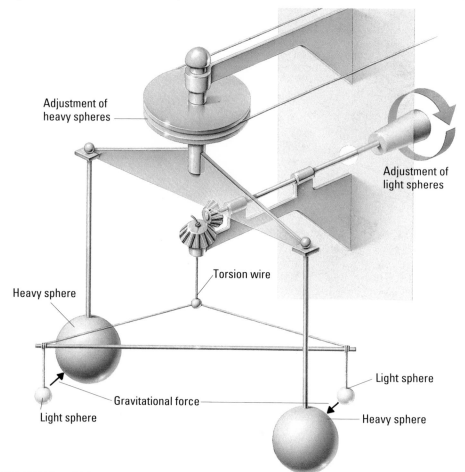

Adjustment of heavy spheres

Adjustment of light spheres

Torsion wire

Heavy sphere

Light sphere

Gravitational force

Light sphere

Light sphere

Heavy sphere

TORSION

The British physicist Henry Cavendish used an apparatus (left), called a torsion balance, to measure the force of gravity. The gravitational force of attraction between a pair of light spheres and a pair of heavy spheres caused a torsion wire to twist. From the amount of twisting, Cavendish calculated the strength of the force.

Torsion is also used in the suspension system of some automobiles. The suspension system contains a bar. As the wheels of the automobile hit small bumps in the road, the force of the bumps is carried to the bar. The bar is twisted by the force and absorbs some of the shock. This makes sure that the passengers in the automobile have a smooth ride.

TORTOISE (tôr′tĭs) *Tortoise* is the name given to a group of reptiles with shells. A tortoise is really a turtle that lives on land (see REPTILE; TURTLE). Tortoises are found in various warm parts of the world. The largest tortoises, up to 550 lb. [250 kg] in weight, live in the Galápagos and Aldabra islands. The Galápagos Islands lie off the coast of Ecuador in South America. The Aldabra Islands lie off eastern Africa. In the United States, tortoises are found mainly in the deserts of the south and southwest and in dry parts of the southeast. The gopher tortoise lives in the southeastern states. The desert tortoise is found in Arizona, California, and Utah and in Mexico.

The tortoise has stumpy, scaly legs. The shell is made of bone with a horny coating of tortoiseshell on the outside. The animal's shell has two main parts. The upper part is like a dome and is called the carapace. The flatter part on the underside is the plastron. The carapace and plastron are usually joined at the sides. There are gaps where the legs stick out. Gaps at the front and rear allow the head and tail to pass through. The ribs and the backbone are firmly set in the carapace, so tortoises cannot breathe in the normal way by moving ribs in and out. Instead, special muscles in the abdomen enlarge and contract the lung cavity. Tortoises have no teeth. They use a horny beak to bite their food. All tortoises feed on plants. During the winter, the animals sleep in holes that they dig. Tortoises are famous for their slow movement and for their long lives. Some of them live for more than a hundred years.

TOUCAN (too′kăn′) The toucan is a stocky bird with short wings. It is found in the forests of Mexico and Central and South America. Toucans are noted chiefly for their large and usually brightly colored bills. In some species, the bill is as long as the rest of the body. The bill looks quite heavy, but it is really very light because it contains many air pockets. A

TORTOISE—Ancient animal
Tortoises have changed very little since they first appeared on earth 200 million years ago. They have probably survived in this way largely because of the protection given to them by their shells.

TORTOISE—Giant tortoise
Tortoises are land turtles. They are found in warm climates throughout the world. The giant tortoise pictured at right makes its home in the Galápagos Islands off the coast of Ecuador in South America.

TOUCAN

The black-billed mountain toucan (left) and the chestnut-mandibled toucan live in the forests of South America.

toucan's bill may be black, blue, brown, green, red, white, yellow, or a combination of colors. Many scientists believe toucans use their bills to attract mates.

About forty species of toucans exist. The largest species is the toco toucan. It measures about 25 in. [64 cm] in length. One of the smaller species is the green aracari. It has a body length of about 13 in. [33 cm].

Toucans feed mainly on small fruit. Sometimes the bird's bill, which has edges like a saw, is used to tear off pieces of large fruit. Most toucans live in family groups or small flocks. The birds usually nest in holes high up in trees.

See also BIRD.

TOUCH Touch is an external sense of the body that tells it when contact is made with an object (see SENSE). Touch is made up of a number of other senses, such as cold, heat, pain, and pressure. These senses respond to stimuli applied to the skin (see STIMULUS). Touch is also called the tactile sense.

There are several kinds of touch organs, called tactile corpuscles, in the skin and mucous membranes (see MUCOUS MEMBRANE; SKIN). One type is found near hairs, another in areas without hair, and still another in deeper tissue. The sensation of touch occurs when an object comes in contact with the touch organs and presses them out of shape or when it comes in contact with a nearby hair. Nerves carry impulses from these touch organs to the brain (see NERVOUS SYSTEM).

Touch is more sensitive in some parts of the body than in other parts. This is because the touch organs are not distributed evenly throughout the body. In some places, the touch organs are found in clusters. For example, the tip of the tongue and the tips of the fingers are very sensitive because of the clusters of touch organs. On the other hand, the area of the body between the shoulder blades contains only a few sense organs per square inch. Therefore, the body is less sensitive there. The particular touch organs for heat, cold, and pain are also distributed unevenly. For example, if a person runs a metal instrument over his or her skin, he or she will find that the instrument feels cold at some points and warm at others. At some points on the skin, the metal instrument is merely felt as a presence. Some objects act upon several senses at once. For example, a hot iron touching the skin causes a person to feel pain, heat, and pressure. **PROJECT 74**

ACTIVITY *Testing touch*

Touch is more sensitive on some parts of the body than others. To investigate this, take a hairpin or a paper clip and bend it into the shape of a "V." Close your eyes and touch various parts of your body with the wire points. Whether you feel one point or two points depends on how sensitive the area is.

TOURMALINE (tŏŏr′mə lĭn) Tourmaline is a mineral that is made up of several elements, including aluminum, boron, and silicon (see ALUMINUM; BORON; MINERAL; SILICON). There are three main kinds of tourmaline: iron-rich black tourmaline; magnesium-rich brown tourmaline; and alkali tourmaline. Alkali tourmaline ranges in color from red to green to blue (see ALKALI; IRON; MAGNESIUM). Some colored tourmalines are used for jewelry. These include the pinkish rubellite and the bluish indicolite.

Tourmaline is usually found in coarse-grained granite. Tourmaline is strongly piezoelectric (see GRANITE; PIEZOELECTRIC EFFECT). The best-known sources of tourmaline are the island of Elba, which lies off the western coast of Italy, and the state of Minas Gerais in Brazil. In the United States, tourmaline is found in Connecticut, southern California, Maine, and Massachusetts.

TOXIC WASTE

Toxic waste includes all substances entering the environment that pose a hazard to the health of plants, animals, or humans. This type of waste is most commonly generated by people through industrial, military, and agricultural activities. Toxic waste includes chemicals such as cyanide, pesticides such as DDT, and metals such as mercury. Because toxic waste is very difficult to remove from the environment, it must be handled carefully and disposed of in special sites. *See also* POLLUTION; WASTE DISPOSAL.

TOXIN

(tŏk′sĭn) Toxins are poisons produced by the normal metabolism of certain organisms (see METABOLISM). Many bacteria produce toxins that cause disease, such as botulism, diphtheria, scarlet fever, and tetanus. Our bodies produce substances called antitoxins to protect us against toxins produced by invading bacteria and other organisms. *See also* ANTITOXIN; BACTERIA; BOTULISM; DISEASE; POISON; SCARLET FEVER; TETANUS.

TRACE ELEMENT

Trace elements are minerals needed in very small amounts by the human body to support life. They include copper, iodine, iron, manganese, and zinc (see MINERAL). Copper makes it possible for the human body to use iron to build hemoglobin, a very important part of red blood cells (see HEMOGLOBIN). Iodine is necessary in order for the thyroid gland to produce the hormone thyroxine (see HORMONE). Manganese and zinc are needed for the normal action of certain enzymes (see ENZYME). Trace elements are usually present in a balanced diet. If there is a lack of one or more trace elements, serious illness may occur. For example, goiter, or swelling of the thyroid gland, occurs in human beings if they do not receive enough iodine. Other animals need the same trace elements that humans do. Plants also need trace elements, but their specific requirements vary from those of humans and other animals. *See also* DIET.

TRACER

A tracer is a substance that is used to follow the movement of other substances. For example, tracers are used to follow the movement of certain chemicals through an organism. They may be used to investigate chemical reactions and biochemical processes (see BIOCHEMISTRY; CHEMICAL REACTION). Tracers may also follow the movement of substances in machines and other equipment. To be effective, the tracer must not interfere with any processes in the organism or equipment. The tracer must also be able to be easily detected. One common method is to use an isotope in place of the normal element that would be used in a reaction, for example, C-13 (see ELEMENT; ISOTOPE). Because the isotope has a different relative atomic mass from the normal element, the tracer can be detected easily. Radioactive isotopes, called radioisotopes, can be used. They can be detected easily because of their radioactivity. *See also* RADIOACTIVITY.

TRACHEA

(trā′kē ə) In land vertebrates (animals with backbones), the trachea, or windpipe, is the tube that carries air to and from the lungs (see LUNG). In human adults, the trachea is about 6 in. [15 cm] long and about 1 in. [2.5 cm] in diameter.

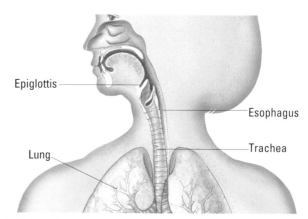

TRACHEA

The trachea, or windpipe, carries air from the throat to the lungs. During eating and swallowing, the epiglottis closes off the trachea so that food passes into the esophagus.

It runs from the larynx (voice box) to the center of the chest, where it splits into two smaller tubes, the bronchi (see LARYNX). The bronchi lead to the lungs. The trachea is kept open by rings of stiff cartilage shaped like horseshoes (see CARTILAGE).

The trachea is lined with mucous membrane that helps moisten the air breathed in (see MUCOUS MEMBRANE). The cells in this membrane have many tiny hairlike structures called cilia (plural of *cilium*) that help trap small particles of dust and dirt (see CILIUM). The trachea also has muscles that can narrow or widen the passageway. During choking or coughing, the trachea narrows to about one-sixth its normal width. As air rushes out through this narrowed passageway, it travels much faster than normal. This helps force out any foreign particles that may be stuck in the trachea.

Insects, spiders, and a few other arthropods also breathe by means of tracheae (plural of *trachea*), although these tracheae are quite different from those of vertebrates. They are fine, branching tubes that spread throughout the body and carry air to all parts. They open at the spiracles, or breathing pores, on the surface of the body.

See also ARACHNID; ARTHROPODA; INSECT; RESPIRATORY SYSTEM; SPIRACLE.

TRADESCANTIA (trăd′ə skăn′ chə) *Tradescantia* is a genus of about 65 species of monocotyledonous herbaceous plants found in North and South America (see HERBACEOUS PLANT;

MONOCOTYLEDON). These perennial plants have clusters of three-petaled flowers. The leaves vary from species to species. Many are trailing plants, often known as spiderworts. Some, such as the wandering jew, are popular houseplants.

See also PERENNIAL PLANT.

TRANQUILIZER (trăng′kwə līz′ər) A tranquilizer is a drug that calms a person's mind by slowing down the activities of the central nervous system. Unlike a sedative, a tranquilizer does not cause sleepiness (see DRUG; NERVOUS SYSTEM; SEDATIVE).

Tranquilizers are used to relieve tension. They have been used to treat many of the symptoms of certain mental illnesses, such as schizophrenia (see MENTAL ILLNESS). They have also been used to reduce high blood pressure. The exact way tranquilizers work is not known. They are believed to affect transmission of nerve signals between certain nerve cells in the brain. If used in large doses for a long period of time, most tranquilizers can be addictive.

See also ADDICTION.

TRANSDUCER (trăns doo′sər) A transducer is a device that changes one kind of signal into another. The signal that it produces varies according to the strength of the first signal. A microphone is an example of a transducer. It changes sound signals into electrical signals (see MICROPHONE). The word *transducer* is most often used for devices that turn sound signals into electrical signals or electrical signals into sound signals. However, transducers also include instruments such as barometers. A barometer changes atmospheric pressure into the movement of a pointer on a scale.

See also BAROMETER.

TRADESCANTIA

Many species of tradescantia are popular houseplants and garden ornamentals.

TRANSFORMER

A transformer is a device that increases or decreases the voltage of an alternating electric current (see ALTERNATING CURRENT; CURRENT, ELECTRIC; VOLT). An alternating current is one that builds up in one direction along a wire. When it reaches its maximum, it starts to decrease until it reaches zero. The current then changes direction. It builds up to its maximum, decreases to zero, and reverses direction again.

Transformers usually contain a core of soft iron. This core may be shaped like a ring or hollow square. Two coils of wire are wound around this core. The coils are kept separate from each other. The source of the voltage to be changed is connected to the coil called the primary winding. The final voltage is supplied by the other coil, called the secondary winding, to a circuit (see CIRCUIT, ELECTRIC). The number of turns of wire in the coils varies. If the primary coil has more turns than the secondary coil, the voltage of the alternating

POWER STATION

Large transformers (below), used at electric power plants, create very high voltages for power supply lines.

TRANSFORMER CONSTRUCTION

A small transformer (above) has two coils of wire wound around a laminated (layered) core made of soft iron.

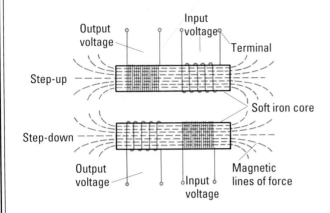

Output voltage · Input voltage · Terminal · Step-up · Soft iron core · Step-down · Output voltage · Input voltage · Magnetic lines of force

TRANSFORMER PRINCIPLE

A transformer (above) is used to increase (step-up) or decrease (step-down) the voltage of an alternating current. The input voltage is applied across the terminals of the primary coil. The primary coil is wrapped around a core of soft iron. The current causes a magnetic field to flow through the iron. The field changes as the current changes. The bar also has another coil wrapped around it. The changing magnetic field induces a current in the secondary coil. If the primary coil has more turns than the secondary coil, the output voltage is stepped-down. If the primary coil has fewer turns, the output voltage is stepped-up.

current is decreased. This kind of transformer is known as a step-down transformer. If the primary coil has fewer turns than the secondary coil, the voltage of the alternating current is increased. This kind of transformer is called a step-up transformer.

When an alternating current is connected to a primary coil, the current flows through the coil. Because the current is changing, it creates a changing magnetic field. This changing magnetic field, in turn, produces a current in the secondary coil. This current is said to be induced (see ELECTROMAGNETISM; INDUCTION; MAGNETIC FIELD). The current flowing in the secondary coil produces a voltage. The size of this voltage depends on the number of turns in the primary and secondary coils.

The iron core consists of a number of layers called laminations. Each layer is insulated from the next by a sheet of paper or a coating of varnish. This insulation prevents voltage from being produced in the core. This would heat the core and waste energy.
See also ELECTRICITY.

SUBSTATION

Transformers at electricity substations (left) convert the high voltage from supply lines to lower voltages for use by homes and industry.

TRANSISTOR

A transistor (trăn zĭs'tər) is a tiny device used to control and amplify (make stronger) an electrical signal. Transistors are now used in place of vacuum tubes in the circuits of most electronic equipment (see ELECTRONICS; VACUUM TUBE). Transistors are smaller, lighter, more dependable, and less expensive than vacuum tubes. Transistors also use much less electricity and give off much less heat than vacuum tubes. Transistors were developed in 1947 by three American physicists: John Bardeen, William Shockley, and Walter Brattain. These three shared the Nobel Prize for physics in 1956.

A transistor is made of a semiconductor, such as silicon or germanium (see SEMICONDUCTOR). Small amounts of certain impurities are added to control the flow of electrical current in the semiconductor (see CURRENT, ELECTRIC). These impurities do one of two things. They may add free electrons that can move about within the semiconductor (see ELECTRON). This type of semiconductor is called n-type (*n* stands for the negatively charged electrons). On the other hand, the impurities may not add enough electrons, leaving a number of positively charged spaces, or holes. These holes, like the electrons, can move about within the semiconductor. This type of semiconductor is called p-type (*p* stands for the positively charged holes).

There are two basic types of transistors—junction and field effect. In a junction transistor, one type of semiconductor is placed between two layers of the other type. If the middle layer is p-type, for example, the outer layers are both n-type. This is called an NPN transistor. The middle layer is the base. One outside layer is the emitter (sender). The other is the collector (receiver). This transistor has two junctions. One junction is where the base and emitter touch. The second junction is where the base and collector touch.

In order for current to flow properly through the NPN transistor, the voltage of the base must be more positive than the voltage of the emitter (see VOLT). The voltage of the collector, in turn, must be more positive than the voltage of the base. In this way, negatively charged electrons move from the emitter through the base to the collector. This flow of electrons causes a current. The number of electrons in the base controls the flow of electrons from the emitter to the collector. A source of voltage connected to the base controls the number of electrons in the base. A slight increase in this voltage to the base will cause a much greater increase in the current flowing from the emitter to the collector. In

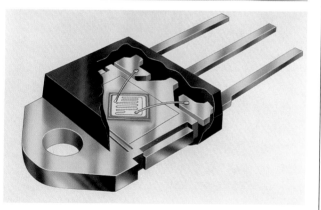

TRANSISTOR TYPES

Transistors vary in size depending on what they are used for. Small transistors, often with wire leads (top), are soldered (joined with melted metal) into holes on printed circuit boards. Microwave transistors (center) are designed to handle high powers. The plug-in type (bottom) is used in engine control units for automobiles and trucks.

SAVING POWER

Transistors use less power than vacuum tubes and give off much less heat. Because transistors are so much smaller than vacuum tubes, electronic circuits using them are also much smaller.

this way, a transistor can amplify a signal to many times its original strength. A signal leaving the collector may be ten thousand times stronger than when it entered the emitter.

Another type of junction transistor, the PNP transistor, contains a layer of n-type semiconductor placed between two layers of p-type semiconductor. This transistor is similar to the NPN transistor. In the PNP transistor, however, it is the positively charged holes (and not electrons) that move from emitter to collector. In the PNP transistor, then, the voltage of the base must be more negative than the voltage of the emitter. The collector, in turn, must be more negative than the base.

In a field effect transistor, there are only two layers of semiconductor. A current flowing through one of the layers, the channel, is controlled by a source of voltage connected to the other layer, the gate.

In the 1960s, scientists developed a way to make many transistors on a single piece of semiconductor material. This led to the development of complete electronic circuits on one semiconductor. These circuits are known as integrated circuits (see INTEGRATED CIRCUIT). Transistors are used in many types of electronic equipment, such as computers, hearing aids, radios, cassette players, televisions, and satellites. Because they require little electricity, transistors have made it possible to operate much of this equipment with energy supplied by small batteries. As a result, many of the kinds of electronic equipment operated by transistors are portable. *See also* BATTERY.

MINIATURIZATION

Integrated circuits—complete electronic circuits on a single semiconductor—make it possible to design small, battery-powered equipment. This portable cassette player is only a little larger than the audio cassette it can play.

TRANSMUTATION OF ELEMENTS

The changing of one element into another is called transmutation. The British physicist Ernest Rutherford did this first in 1919. He changed nitrogen atoms into oxygen atoms (see ATOM; ELEMENT; RUTHERFORD, ERNEST).

All atoms contain a central core called a nucleus (see NUCLEUS). The nucleus contains two types of particles—neutrons and protons (see NEUTRON; PROTON). If two nuclei (plural of *nucleus*) of the same element contain different numbers of neutrons, they are known as isotopes (see ISOTOPE). However, if two nuclei contain different numbers of protons, they are nuclei of different elements. The number of protons in the nucleus determines the element to which that nucleus belongs. Therefore, to transmute an element, the number of protons in the nucleus has to be changed. This can be done by bombarding the nucleus with such particles as protons or alpha particles (see ALPHA PARTICLE). When these particles collide with the nucleus, a nuclear reaction may take place. In a nuclear reaction, the nucleus absorbs the particles. Then, one or more particles may be given off by the nucleus.

An example of the transmutation of elements is Rutherford's experiment. When he fired alpha particles at nitrogen, the nitrogen nuclei absorbed the alpha particles and gave off protons. This reaction changed the nitrogen atoms into oxygen atoms.

The transmutation of elements sometimes occurs naturally. This happens with radioactive elements. When a radioactive element decays, it often changes into a different element.
See also ACCELERATORS, PARTICLE; RADIOACTIVITY.

TRANSPIRATION (trăn′spə rā′shən) Transpiration is the process in which a plant gives off water as water vapor. Most of this water vapor is lost through the stomata (plural of *stoma*). Stomata are openings in the lower epidermis of a leaf (see LEAF; STOMA; VAPOR). Transpiration increases when the roots have enough water, the temperature is neither very high nor very low, there is a slight breeze, and there is bright sunlight.

Transpiration is the final step in the journey of water from the roots, through the stem, and into the leaves. As cells in the surface layers of the leaf lose water, they draw water from neighboring cells by osmosis (see OSMOSIS). This cell-to-cell movement extends back through the leaf, to the stem, and to the roots, forming a continuous column of water. The pulling of the leaves is great enough to transport water from the roots to the top of a tall tree.

About 98 percent of the water drawn up from the roots is lost through transpiration. A 30-ft. [9-m] oak tree can lose about 44 gallons [200 liters] of water on a warm summer day, and a large tree can give off many tons of water during the course of a year. This seems a great waste, but it is the only way plants can get water and dissolved minerals up to the leaves, where they are needed to make new food materials. *See also* PHOTOSYNTHESIS. PROJECT 69

TRANSPLANT A transplant is a section of body tissue or a complete body organ that is removed from its original site and transferred to a new position. The transplant can be from one place in a person's body to another, called an autograft, or from one individual to another, called a heterograft. The procedure by which this is done is called transplantation (see TRANSPLANTATION). Plastic surgery and other branches of surgery have developed the transfer of skin, muscle, bone, and bone marrow, and even entire organs such as the heart, kidney, and lungs (see HEART; KIDNEY; LUNGS; PLASTIC SURGERY; SURGERY). A blood transfusion is a form of transplant that is very common (see BLOOD TRANSFUSION). About 150,000 major organs have now been transplanted worldwide. This has been made possible partly through successes in preventing rejection of the transplant (attack of the new organ by the body's immune system), through building up organ banks, through improving procedures of transplantation, and through improving techniques to preserve the transplant after it has been removed from the donor.

TRANSPLANTATION In medicine, transplantation is a surgical operation in which a tissue or an organ is replaced with a similar structure from another part of the body or from another person's body (see ORGAN; SURGERY; TISSUE; TRANSPLANT). The original tissue or organ may have been harmed

TRANSPLANTATION

This man has had a bone marrow transplant. Until the new marrow begins to produce white blood cells, he must stay in a sterile environment at the hospital to avoid infection.

by disease, injury, or genetic error (see HEREDITY). Replacement of a defective structure with a synthetic (human-made) structure is called implantation (see IMPLANTATION).

There are several problems with transplantation. The most serious of these problems is rejection. Rejection is common when an organ is transplanted from one person's body into another's body. The body reacts to the transplanted organ as though it were an infection (see INFECTION). Whenever any foreign substance enters the body, the body tries to protect itself. The body makes antibodies and sends immune system cells to attack and try to destroy the transplanted organ (see ANTIBODY; IMMUNITY). This is the main reason that many transplants fail after a few months or years.

Various drugs and X rays that keep immune system cells from working or being produced are sometimes used to prevent rejection. However, this blocks the body's defense against infections. In the 1980s, doctors began using a drug called cyclosporine during transplants. Cyclosporine temporarily blocks the immune system cells called helper T cells from being produced without blocking the work of the rest of the immune system. However, the drug is expensive and can have dangerous side effects. Researchers are still searching for a treatment that will not only prevent rejection of transplants but also build the body's ability to

tolerate the transplant after the treatment is stopped. *See also* BARNARD, CHRISTIAAN NEETHLING; MEDICAL ENGINEERING; PLASTIC SURGERY.

TRANSURANIC ELEMENT (trăns'yoo răn'ĭk ĕl'ə mənt) All atoms contain a central core called a nucleus. The nucleus is made up of two kinds of particles called protons and neutrons (see ATOM; NEUTRON; NUCLEUS; PROTON). The number of protons in the nucleus of an element determines the atomic number of that element (see ELEMENT). A transuranic element is any element that has an atomic number greater than 92, the atomic number of uranium. The first transuranic element is neptunium, with an atomic number of 93. Next is plutonium, with an atomic number of 94. Plutonium is an important element because it is used as a fuel in some nuclear reactors. It is also used in nuclear weapons (see NUCLEAR ENERGY; NUCLEAR WEAPONS; PLUTONIUM; URANIUM).

All the transuranic elements are radioactive (see RADIOACTIVITY). This is because their nuclei (plural of *nucleus*) are so heavy that they are unstable. Only one of them, plutonium, exists naturally on Earth. The rest have to be made artificially. This is done by a process known as transmutation of elements (see TRANSMUTATION OF ELEMENTS). Only the elements with atomic numbers up to 110 have been made. However, physicists are trying to make an element with an atomic number of 114.

TRANSVERSE WAVE A transverse wave is a wave in which the wave vibrations move at right angles to the direction in which the wave is traveling (see WAVE). An example of a transverse wave is the waves seen on a pond when a stone is thrown into the still water. Circular waves spread out from the point where the stone entered the water. However, the water is not traveling outward. The surface of the water merely moves up and down as the wave passes. The surface moves at right angles to the direction in which the wave is traveling, thus the waves are transverse waves.

Waves in which the vibrations move in the direction that the wave is traveling are called longitudinal waves (see LONGITUDINAL WAVE). Sound waves are longitudinal waves (see SOUND).

A tree is any tall, woody plant that continues to grow each year (see WOODY PLANT). Trees usually grow with one main stem, called a trunk, and several branches that grow outward or upward at a distance above the ground. Woody plants that usually grow with several main stems are called shrubs (see SHRUB). Trees are found wherever there is enough warmth and moisture. They are not found in polar regions; cold, dry regions called tundra; some mountaintops; and extremely arid (dry) lands.

Kinds of trees There are two main kinds of trees: flowering trees, called angiosperms, and cone-bearing trees, called conifers. Conifers belong to the group of plants called gymnosperms (see ANGIOSPERM; CONIFER; GYMNOSPERM). Angiosperms are also known as broad-leaved trees because their leaves are usually broad in comparison with the leaves of conifers. Most broad-leaved trees in temperate regions are deciduous (see DECIDUOUS TREE). Conifers are sometimes called needle-leaved trees. Most conifers are evergreens (see EVERGREEN). In the lumber industry, needle-leaved trees are known as softwoods. Broad-leaved trees are called hardwoods (see LUMBER).

Conifers, including pines and spruces, are usually most abundant in cooler regions, although they also grow well in areas with hot, dry summers—as long as there is plenty of rain in winter. The tough needles of conifers are well adapted for life in such climates. The small surface area, the tough coat, and the sunken stoma all reduce evaporation from the leaves (see LEAF; STOMA). This helps the trees grow where water is scarce. Conifers grow in forests in northern regions and on mountains, where low temperatures prevent the roots from absorbing water quickly. Smaller coniferous forests grow

TRANSPORT SYSTEM

The cells that form tissues in the trunks and branches of a tree make up a biological transport system. Xylem tissue carries water and minerals upwards from the roots. Phloem tissue carries food (glucose) from the leaves to other parts of the plant.

CONIFERS

Most conifers (cone-bearing trees) are evergreens and, like the cedar of Lebanon (left), keep their leaves throughout the year. But the leaves of the swamp cypress (above) change color to a deep red in the fall.

around the Mediterranean Sea and in parts of Florida and California, where summer drought (lack of rainfall) limits the water supply.

Angiosperms reach their greatest development in temperate zones and in wet tropical areas (see CLIMATE). Species growing in the temperate forests are nearly all deciduous. They include beeches, elms, hickories, maples, and many kinds of oaks. Angiosperms in tropical rain forests are nearly all evergreens. With a constant high temperature and a constant supply of water, they can grow throughout the year (see RAIN FOREST). There are two main groups of angiosperms—dicotyledons and monocotyledons—but, apart from the palms, nearly all the trees are dicotyledons (see DICOTYLEDON; MONOCOTYLEDON).

A typical tree Like other seed-bearing plants, trees start as seeds (see SEED). After germination, the seed produces a small herbaceous seedling that soon becomes woody (see GERMINATION; HERBA-CEOUS PLANT). The actively dividing cambium cells, which are found in the stems and roots, form a complete ring inside the young stem. These cells begin to form phloem tissue and xylem tissue. The xylem carries water and dissolved minerals from the roots to the leaves. The phloem carries food from the leaves toward the roots (see CAMBIUM; PHLOEM; XYLEM). The stem eventually forms a trunk as it gets thicker and taller. The extra thickness is caused almost entirely by the buildup of xylem, made by the cambium, year after year. This buildup forms the rings of the tree (see ANNUAL RING). The deli-cate phloem tissues break down after a while. At any given time, there is only a narrow band of phloem around the trunk under the outer bark (see BARK). The older or inner xylem becomes plugged with substances that stop the flow of water and minerals. It becomes the heartwood (see HEART-WOOD). The younger, outer xylem continues to carry water and minerals and is known as sapwood.

The bark of a tree protects it from temperature changes and other damage. It develops early in the life of a tree, when cells just under the epidermis (outer layer) of the young plant develop waterproof cell walls. These cells are called cork cells. The bark grad-ually gets thicker as cell layers deeper down in the stem become corky. The phloem is often called the inner bark. The outer bark is dead because the cork walls of the cells are airtight and watertight. Lenticels, or breathing pores, are openings in the outer bark

TREE SHAPES

The shape of a given type of tree may vary, depending on where it grows. A Scots pine growing alone (above) has a domed shape, unlike the spindly form of Scots pines growing closely together in a group (right).

through which air containing oxygen enters and leaves. The outer bark crumbles away throughout a tree's life. The bark of most trees crumbles slowly. It becomes deeply furrowed as the tree gets thicker. The bark of the beech tree, however, never gets thick because it crumbles almost as rapidly as it forms. Many trees are recognized by the pattern of their bark.

As the tree gets older and larger, it produces branches. A tree in the middle of a forest, with other trees around it, does not usually have many branches on the lower parts of the trunk. A tree growing in a cleared area, however, may have branches near the ground. Large trees may weigh many tons. They need a good root system to anchor them. The roots do not always go deeply into the ground, but they do spread widely (see ROOT).

Palm trees are native to many of the warmer parts of the world. They are monocotyledons, and they grow in a different way from other trees. Their xylem and phloem tissues are grouped in bundles scattered through the trunk instead of in rings. The trunks grow taller each year but they do not get thicker or have annual rings. They do not normally branch, and the leaves all grow in a big cluster at the top of the trunk. The timber and leaves of palm trees provide important building materials in the tropics.

Trees are the largest of all plants. In fact, they are the largest of all living things. Some of the giant redwoods and sequoias of California weigh over 2,000 tons. The life of a tree varies greatly, but some trees live for hundreds or even thousands of years—much longer than any other living thing. Some conifers recently discovered in Tasmania are thought to be well over 10,000 years old.

See also PLANT KINGDOM; SAPWOOD; WOOD.

STRANGE TREES

Over millions of years, some trees have evolved strange forms. The baobab (below) grows on the savannas of Africa. Its trunk may be as wide as the trunk of a giant redwood, although the tree is much shorter. Another African tree, the senecio (bottom left), grows in alpine conditions in the mountains of Kenya. The fernlike cycad (bottom right) is one of the oldest seed plants, dating from 200 million years ago.

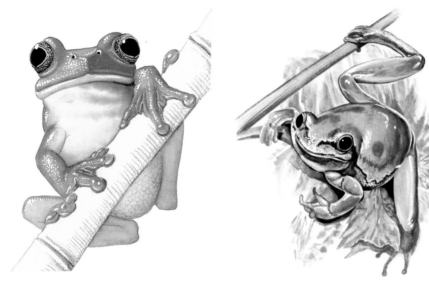

TREE FROG
Tree frogs live mainly in trees. They cling to branches with the sticky pads on their feet. Most tree frogs can change color to match their surroundings.

TREE FROG Tree frogs live mainly in trees and shrubs. There are several hundred kinds of tree frogs. They all have sticky pads on their feet. These pads allow the animals to cling to leaves as they leap from one branch to another. Most tree frogs can change color (see CAMOUFLAGE). Tree frogs feed chiefly on insects.

Tree frogs, which belong to the family Hylidae, live in North and South America and most other warm parts of the world. Tree frogs are usually heard more than they are seen. One kind of tree frog is called a peeper. It can be heard on early spring days and warm winter days calling from near waterways or marshes. Most tree frogs come down from the trees to lay their eggs in ponds, but some breed in tiny pools of water trapped in holes in trees.
See also FROG.

TRIASSIC PERIOD (trī ăs′ĭk pĭr′ē əd) The Triassic period began about 245 million years ago and lasted about 37 million years. It is the earliest division of the Mesozoic era.

During the Triassic, there were many kinds of reptiles, and the first dinosaurs appeared. Crocodiles and turtles also emerged during the Triassic. The first mammals developed at this time, possibly from mammal-like reptiles. There were many insects and fish as well. Plant life became more widespread toward the end of the Triassic.

Much sediment was deposited on the earth's continents during the Triassic period. Faults formed in eastern North America.

See also DINOSAUR; FAULT; GEOLOGICAL TIME SCALE; MESOZOIC ERA; SEDIMENTARY ROCK.

TRICEPS (trī′sĕps′) The triceps is one of the muscles in the upper part of the arm. It runs from the shoulder to the elbow and is located on the opposite side of the arm from the biceps brachii muscle. The biceps is the muscle that bulges when the arm is bent. It allows the arm to bend and is called a flexor muscle. The triceps straightens the arm. It is called an extensor muscle.
See also BICEPS; MUSCLE.

TRICHINOSIS (trĭk′ ə nō′sĭs) Trichinosis is the infection caused by trichina, a parasitic nematode (see NEMATODE; PARASITE). Trichinas are about 0.056 to 0.064 in. [1.4 to 1.6 mm] long. They live in the small intestines of mammals, including badgers, cats, dogs, muskrats, pigs, raccoons, rodents, and human beings (see MAMMAL). A female trichina may give birth to 1,500 larvae. The blood of the animal in which the trichina lives spreads the larvae throughout its body (see LARVA). These larvae burrow into muscle tissue and surround themselves with a tough capsule. If the muscle tissue is eaten by another mammal, the larvae grow into adults and live in the intestines.

Humans often get trichinosis by eating the infected meat of pigs (pork). To prevent infection, all pork should be well-cooked before eating. Trichinosis does not kill many people. However, it can cause muscular pain and stiffness, fever, sweating, and insomnia (lack of sleep).

TRIGONOMETRY

Trigonometry (trĭg′ ə nŏm′ ĭ trē) is a branch of mathematics dealing with the relationships between the sides and angles of triangles. It was first used in astronomy and navigation. Today, trigonometry is widely used by scientists and engineers as well (see ASTRONOMY; ENGINEERING; GEOMETRY; MATHEMATICS; NAVIGATION).

Trigonometry involves ratios when dealing with the relationship between sides and angles of triangles (see RATIO). In the diagram below, O is the center of a circle. The radius of the circle is the line OP. P is a point on the circumference of the circle. The angle POX is labeled θ.

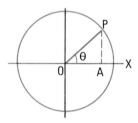

As the line OP rotates about O, the degree of the angle increases from 0° to 360° after a complete turn (see DEGREE). If a line PA is drawn from P at right angles to line OX, both the lengths, OA and AP, change as the angle θ changes. The ratio PA/OP is called the sine of the angle. The ratio OA/OP is called the cosine of the angle. They are written as $\sin\theta$ and $\cos\theta$ respectively. The ratio PA/OA is called the tangent of the angle. It is written as $\tan\theta$. $\sin\theta/\cos\theta$ also gives the tangent of the angle.

As the angle increases from 0° to 90°, $\sin\theta$ increases from 0 (zero) to 1. As the angle continues

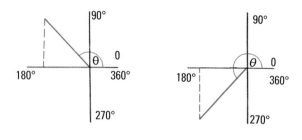

to increase to 180°, $\sin\theta$ decreases back to 0. From 180° to 270°, $\sin\theta$ decreases from 0 to -1 and then moves back to 0 as the angle increases to 360°.

The values of $\sin\theta$ are repeated after each complete turn. The way $\sin\theta$ changes can be shown on a graph.

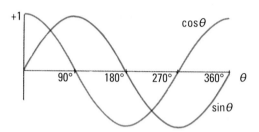

The cosine behaves in a similar way. However, the cosine starts at 1 when the angle is 0° and decreases to 0 as the angle increases to 90°.

Tables have been made to give values of sin, cos, and tan for angles up to 90°.

If the value of one of the angles of a triangle and the length of one side are known, the other lengths can be worked out by using these relationships. For example, let AB = 5 cm and θ = 60°.

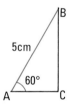

BC/AB = $\sin\theta$, so BC = 5 x sin 60°
 = 5 x 0.866
 (from tables of sines)
 = 4.33 cm

In the same way, using the cosine ratio, the length of AC can be found. From Pythagoras, it is known that $AB^2 = AC^2 + BC^2$.

See also PYTHAGOREAN THEOREM.

TRILOBITE

Trilobites were arthropods that lived in the Paleozoic era. They became extinct between 290 and 245 million years ago.

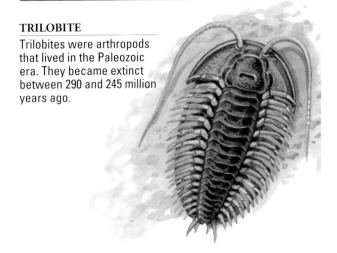

TRILOBITE (trī′lə bīt′) A trilobite is an extinct arthropod that lived during the Paleozoic era. The Paleozoic era began 570 million years ago and ended 245 million years ago. Most trilobites were about 4 in. [10 cm] long, but some grew to lengths of about 2 ft. [60 cm] (see ARTHROPODA; EXTINCTION; PALEOZOIC ERA).

Trilobites lived on the seafloor and dug into the mud for food. They were named trilobites because their shells were divided into three lobes. The thorax of the trilobite was also divided into segments. Each segment had legs. The gills of the trilobite were located on its legs (see GILLS; THORAX).

More than ten thousand species of trilobites have been identified by studying their fossils. Trilobites flourished during the Cambrian and Ordovician periods, but became extinct during the Permian period.

See also FOSSIL; GEOLOGICAL TIME SCALE.

TROPIC (trŏp′ĭk) A tropic is either of two lines of latitude that are located at 23°27′ from the equator (see EQUATOR; LATITUDE AND LONGITUDE). The tropic of Cancer, at 23°27′N, marks the northernmost latitude where the sun can appear directly overhead. The tropic of Capricorn, at 23°27′S, marks the southernmost latitude where the sun can ever appear directly overhead.

TROPIC

The tropics occupy a band spanning the equator between the tropics of Cancer and Capricorn (left). Much of the land in the tropics contains rain forests (above), where warm temperatures and an abundance of water make for lush plant growth. Tropical rain forests are home to large numbers of animal as well as plant species. Many of these species are seriously endangered by the widespread destruction of the rain forests.

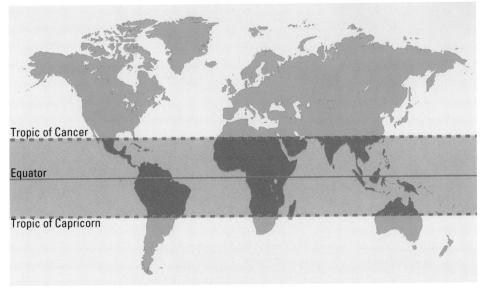

Tropic of Cancer

Equator

Tropic of Capricorn

In the Northern Hemisphere, the day that the sun appears directly overhead at the tropic of Cancer is called the summer solstice. It occurs on June 20 or 21. In the Northern Hemisphere, the day the sun appears directly overhead at the tropic of Capricorn is called the winter solstice. It occurs on December 21 or 22. The seasons are reversed in the Southern Hemisphere (see SOLSTICE).

The area between the tropic of Cancer and the tropic of Capricorn is called the tropics. The tropics are characterized by warm temperatures all year. Some areas of the tropics experience wet and dry seasons. Cold weather is found only in the highest mountains. Much of the land in the tropics contains rain forests. There are many kinds of animals and plants in the tropics.
See also RAIN FOREST.

TROPOSPHERE AND TROPOPAUSE

The troposphere is the part of the atmosphere that is closest to the ground (see ATMOSPHERE). It is the densest portion, containing about 75 percent of the mass of the atmosphere but only 1.5 percent of its volume. The temperature of the air in the troposphere decreases with increasing altitude.

The troposphere is the most important layer of the atmosphere because it contains all the air we breathe. It is also the layer in which all the weather and climate conditions occur, and it contains nearly all of the atmosphere's water vapor. Its upper boundary is called the tropopause and lies at a height of about 11 mi. [18 km] above the equator and about 5 mi. [8 km] above the poles. Above the tropopause is the stratosphere.
See also IONOSPHERE; STRATOSPHERE.

TROUT A trout is a fish that belongs to the family Salmonidae. It is closely related to the salmon (see SALMON). The trout is a graceful fish that can only live in cold, clean water. There are ten species of trout found in North America. The best-known species are the eastern brook trout, rainbow trout, and brown trout. The brook trout is native to the northeastern portion of North America. The rainbow trout is native to the western part of North America. The brown trout is native to Europe and Asia but was brought into North American waters.

All trout have been widely distributed because many people like to fish for them. Each year, millions of trout are raised in hatcheries and placed in fishing streams. Trout are known for their leaping ability.

Trout are usually slender, sleek fish. The size of each species varies. Rainbow trout average 12 to 18 in. [30 to 45 cm] in length. Trout that live in large, deep lakes may grow larger. The rainbow trout was named for the red and gold colors along its side. Its body has many small spots, which make the fish hard to see in rocky streams (see CAMOUFLAGE). All trout eat a variety of animals, but young trout mainly eat insects.

Trout that breed in streams near the ocean often go out to sea, and may spend nearly all their adult

TROUT
The rainbow trout, named for its range of colors, is native to the western part of North America. It has also been taken to European waters. It is popular with fishers in both continents.

lives in the ocean (see MIGRATION). These so-called sea trout grow larger than the trout living in streams. Some grow to 50 in. [127 cm] in length and weigh up to 30 lb. [14 kg].

TRYPANOSOME (trĭ păn′ə sōm′) Trypanosomes are a group of parasitic protozoans (see PARASITE; PROTOZOAN). These one-celled organisms are able to swim by using their whiplike flagella (see FLAGELLUM). Most trypanosomes live in the blood or spinal fluid of mammals and other vertebrates (animals with backbones), such as fishes and birds. Most species spend part of their lives inside certain insects.

Several species cause diseases in the animals in which they live. For example, *Trypanosoma gambiense*, a trypanosome carried and spread by the tsetse fly, causes African sleeping sickness. Although most wild animals in Africa have developed an immunity to this disease, domestic animals and people have not. People with sleeping sickness become very drowsy.

See also IMMUNITY; SLEEPING SICKNESS; TSETSE FLY.

TSETSE FLY The tsetse (tsĕt′sē) flies of the genus *Glossina* are blood-sucking flies (see FLY). There are about twenty species, and they all live in Africa. They are about 0.5 in. [1.2 cm] long and have a sharp, needlelike proboscis, or snout. A tsetse fly jabs its proboscis into a victim—usually a mammal—and begins sucking blood. Both male and female tsetse flies feed on blood. Many attack human beings. Tsetse flies are especially dangerous because many carry parasites called trypanosomes that cause disease (see TRYPANOSOME). These diseases may kill human beings, cattle, horses, and other domestic animals. Many wild animals, however, have developed immunity to these diseases (see IMMUNITY).

The reproduction of tsetse flies is unusual because the female lays a larva, not an egg (see LARVA). A single fertilized egg hatches and develops into the larva inside the female's body (see EGG; FERTILIZATION; REPRODUCTION). During this time, the female must have at least three blood meals to nourish the developing larva. The female then lays the fully grown larva. The larva becomes a pupa almost immediately and then an adult shortly afterward.

See also INSECT; METAMORPHOSIS.

TSUNAMI (tsoō nä′mē) A tsunami is a great ocean wave caused by an underwater earthquake or by a hurricane far out in the sea (see EARTHQUAKE; HURRICANE). Tsunamis are sometimes mistakenly called tidal waves. Earthquakes with a Richter scale reading of at least 6.5 that occur less than 30 mi. [50 km] beneath the ocean floor are the most common causes of tsunamis. By using seismographs, scientists can often predict when a tsunami will reach land (see RICHTER SCALE; SEISMOLOGY).

A tsunami in the middle of an ocean is hard to tell from the regular waves. As it nears the shore, however, the coastal waters move back, uncovering an area of seafloor. The water then piles up into a huge wave. This wave sometimes reaches 50 ft. [15 m] before crashing onto land. Tsunamis cause much destruction and death. A huge tsunami destroyed much of the city of Lisbon, Portugal, in 1775.

TUBER A tuber is an underground stem or root that is swollen with a supply of stored food. Stem tubers have several small buds called eyes. These buds obtain their food from the tuber as they grow into new shoots. The new shoots then develop their own tubers. The potato is a popular stem tuber.

See also STEM; VEGETATIVE PROPAGATION.

TUBER

Tubers are swollen underground stems that contain stored food material. The potato plant at right has four tubers.

TUBERCULOSIS (tŏŏ bûr′kyə lō′sĭs) Tuberculosis is a serious infectious disease that usually attacks the lungs (see DISEASE; INFECTION; LUNG). It can require many months or years to cure. Tuberculosis, or TB, is caused by a bacterium (singular of *bacteria*) called a tubercle bacillus. These bacteria travel in tiny droplets of moisture in the air. Sometimes, they are found in contaminated food or milk (see BACTERIA).

When a person breathes in or eats these bacteria, they lodge in the lung tissue. The body soon builds a wall of cells and fiber around the bacteria to confine them. A small, hard lump called a tubercle forms. The bacteria are not killed, but they cannot harm the body as long as this wall remains unbroken. This stage is known as a primary infection. People who have it seldom know it.

There is a danger that when the body's defenses are weaker, such as in old age, the wall can break down. The bacteria will be free to multiply. The body's defenses may not be able to build a wall around the bacteria. In this case, the bacteria will multiply immediately and begin killing lung tissue. The dead tissue is a soft, pink mass that the victim coughs up. This leaves a small cavity, or hole, in the tissue of the lung. Symptoms of the advanced stages of the disease include chest pain, fever, fatigue, weight loss, and loss of appetite.

Skin tests are one way to find out if a person has the tuberculosis bacteria. A small amount of the dead bacteria is injected into the skin. If the person is already infected, the skin around the point of injection becomes hard.

Chemotherapy is the most common treatment. Chemotherapy is the use of drugs for medical treatment. In some cases, X rays are used in addition to chemotherapy (see DRUG; X RAY).

Tuberculosis is far from being conquered. During the mid-1980s, about 22,000 new cases were reported each year in the United States. Deaths caused by tuberculosis in the United States have decreased to about 1,700 each year. About 3 million people worldwide die from tuberculosis each year. However, numbers of cases and deaths have begun to increase greatly.

TULIP The tulip is a flower belonging to the lily family. Tulips grow from bulbs (see BULB AND CORM; LILY FAMILY). There are about 80 species, most of them native to Turkey and Iran. Some have been cultivated for over 600 years. Tulips are now grown all over the United States and in most other

TULIP
Tulips were originally taken to Europe from Turkey and Iran, up to 600 years ago. Today they are grown in many parts of the world. The name *tulip* comes from the Turkish word for *turban*, referring to the shape of the flower.

parts of the world. The country of the Netherlands (Holland) is famous for growing tulips and shipping tulip bulbs all over the world. Farmers in the Netherlands grow nearly two thousand varieties of tulips in a wide range of colors and shapes. Holland, Michigan, is the center of tulip growing in the United States.

Tulip bulbs are planted in autumn. The flowers bloom in the spring. Stems grow up to about 2 ft. [60 cm] high. A brightly colored flower that is shaped like a bell blooms at the tip of the stem. *See also* FLOWER.

TULIP TREE The tulip tree is a tall, deciduous tree that belongs to the magnolia family. It is not related to the tulip (see DECIDUOUS TREE; MAGNOLIA FAMILY; TULIP).

The tulip tree is native to North America. It sometimes reaches a height of more than 190 ft. [58 m]. Its lobed leaves turn yellow in the fall. Its tulip-shaped flowers have six yellowish green petals with orange bases (see FLOWER; LEAF). The tulip tree's hard, yellowish wood is used in furniture and paneling. The tulip tree is sometimes called the yellow

TULIP TREE
The tulip tree is not related to the tulip. It gets its name from its tulip-shaped flowers.

poplar, but it is not related to the true poplars. *See also* POPLAR.

TUNA A tuna is a fish that lives in the ocean and belongs to the family Scombridae. It is closely related to the mackerel (see MACKEREL). The tuna has a thick body and a crescent-shaped tail. It has a line of small fins along the top and bottom of its body. Tuna can swim very fast. They make long migrations in the oceans (see MIGRATION). There are thirteen species of tuna. Several of them are popular game and food fishes. *See also* FISH.

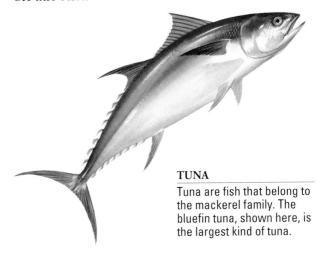

TUNA
Tuna are fish that belong to the mackerel family. The bluefin tuna, shown here, is the largest kind of tuna.

TUNDRA Tundra is a type of treeless land found around the Arctic Circle, farther north than the great coniferous forests of Canada and Siberia. For most of the year, the temperatures are below freezing. The soil beneath the surface does not have a chance to thaw out during the short summers, causing a condition known as permafrost (see PERMAFROST). The brief, cool summers melt the surface ice, forming marshes and lakes and resulting in swarms of mosquitoes and other insects and the rapid growth of plants. Coarse grasses and shallow-rooted low-growing shrubs such as crowberry, bilberry, and bearberry are the typical vegetation, along with mosses and lichens. Caribou and musk ox migrate across the tundra in the summer. Plant decay is slow, so the soil consists of an acid peat.

The expansion and contraction of the soil because of the frost forces stones to the surface, where they are deposited in ring-shaped structures. Another common sight is a pingo—a small hill

TUNDRA
During the short northern summer, permafrost at the surface of the tundra melts. In only a few weeks, plants grow, flower, and produce seeds.

with a core of ice pushed upward to heights of about 140 ft. [40 m]. In Canada and Alaska, such a marshy landscape is also known as muskeg.

TUNGSTEN Tungsten (W) is a heavy, gray metallic element (see ELEMENT). Tungsten was discovered in 1783 by two Spanish chemists, Fausto and Juan José de Elhuyar. It occurs in the mineral wolframite and is sometimes called wolfram. It is also found in other minerals, such as scheelite (see MINERAL). Tungsten is very resistant to corrosion and is ideal for making the filaments in electric light bulbs. It is also used in making very hard alloys (see ALLOY; CORROSION; ELECTRIC LIGHT). Tungsten alloys are used in high-speed cutting tools.

Tungsten forms an acid called tungstic acid (H_2WO_4). The salts of this acid are called tungstates. They are used in fireproofing and dyeing (see ACID; SALTS).

Tungsten's atomic number is 74, and its relative atomic mass is 183.85. Tungsten melts at 6,170°F [3,400°C]. This is the highest melting point of any metal. It boils at about 10,220°F [5,600°C]. Its relative density is 19.3.
See also RELATIVE DENSITY.

TUNING FORK A tuning fork is a device that produces a note of an exact pitch. It is made up of a metal bar attached to two arms. This is why it is called a fork. The base of the fork can be placed on a surface to make the note sound louder. The note produced is very pure and contains only a small amount of other notes mixed with it. For this reason, tuning forks are very useful for tuning musical instruments. Today electronic devices that measure the frequency of sound waves are also used to tune musical instruments.
See also SOUND.

TUNGSTEN
Very hard alloys containing tungsten are used in high-speed cutting tools, such as this drill for making holes in masonry.

TURBINE

A turbine (tûr'bĭn) is a machine that changes the energy of a moving gas or liquid into work that can be used to run machinery. In its simplest form, a turbine is made up of a wheel mounted on a shaft. A series of blades are set around the wheel. When these blades are struck by the gas or liquid, the wheel rotates. This, in turn, makes the shaft rotate. The shaft then drives a machine, such as a generator (see GENERATOR, ELECTRICAL; PROPELLER). The gas or liquid used in a turbine is known as the working medium.

In water turbines, water from a waterfall or a dam is used to drive the turbine (see DAM; WATER-FALL AND RAPID). There are two different methods of making the wheels of the turbine rotate. A jet of water may be directed onto the blades to make the rotor spin. This is called an impulse turbine. The water may be made to flow past blades that are submerged in the flowing water so that it pushes the blades and makes the rotor spin. This is called a reaction turbine (see HYDRO-ELECTRIC POWER).

In a steam turbine, the steam must first be produced by heating water in boilers. The high-pressured steam enters the turbine. Inside the turbine, there is a series of wheels mounted on a shaft. Each wheel is slightly larger in diameter than the one before. This is because the steam expands gradually as it moves through the turbine. The larger wheels make efficient use of the expanding steam. This steam drives the wheels

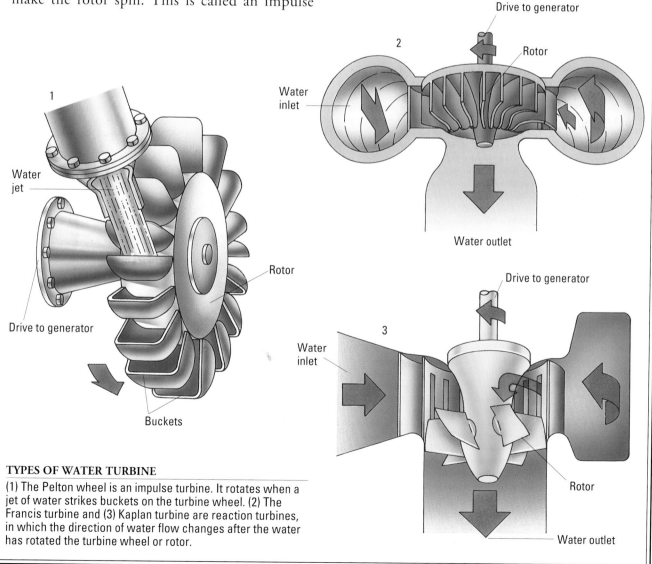

TYPES OF WATER TURBINE

(1) The Pelton wheel is an impulse turbine. It rotates when a jet of water strikes buckets on the turbine wheel. (2) The Francis turbine and (3) Kaplan turbine are reaction turbines, in which the direction of water flow changes after the water has rotated the turbine wheel or rotor.

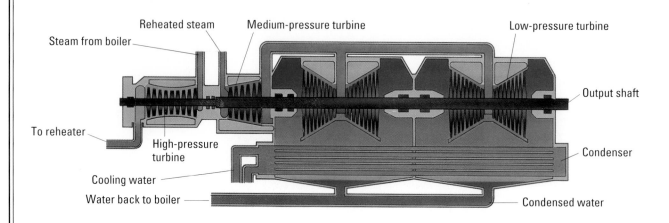

Steam from boiler — Reheated steam — Medium-pressure turbine — Low-pressure turbine — Output shaft — To reheater — High-pressure turbine — Cooling water — Condenser — Water back to boiler — Condensed water

STEAM TURBINE

A modern steam turbine has three stages that use high-pressure, medium-pressure, and low-pressure steam in turn. After leaving the low-pressure turbine, the steam enters a condenser where it is turned back into water, to be reused in a boiler to make more steam.

around (see EXPANSION). In an impulse steam turbine, there is a ring of nozzles in front of each wheel. These nozzles direct the steam onto the blades of the wheel at a certain angle for maximum effect. After leaving a condensing turbine, the steam is cooled and changed back into water. Because water takes up much less space than

steam, a vacuum is created. This vacuum forces more steam to move through the turbine (see VACUUM). In a noncondensing turbine, the steam is used to provide heat.

Gas turbines use hot gases. The gases are produced by burning fuel, such as oil, kerosene, or natural gas. Air is drawn into the front of the turbine and passed through a compressor (see COMPRESSOR). The compressed air is mixed with the fuel, and the mixture is ignited in a combustion chamber. This produces hot, expanding gases, which drive the turbine wheels. Because the turbine and the compressor are mounted on the same shaft, part of the power produced by the

ACTIVITY   *How to make a turbine*

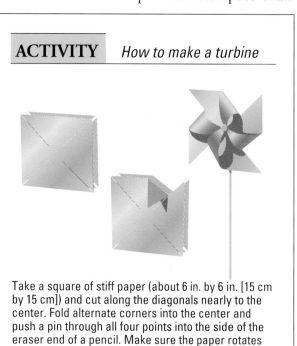

Take a square of stiff paper (about 6 in. by 6 in. [15 cm by 15 cm]) and cut along the diagonals nearly to the center. Fold alternate corners into the center and push a pin through all four points into the side of the eraser end of a pencil. Make sure the paper rotates freely. Blow on your wind turbine and watch it revolve.
Caution: Handle the sharp pin carefully.

ELECTRICITY GENERATION

Most large turbines are used to turn electric generators. The Kaplan turbines (left) are part of a hydroelectric plant. The generators—horizontal blue cylinders (above)—are connected to the drive shafts of steam turbines.

turbine can be used to drive the compressor.

Gas turbines are used in jet engines. The hot gases are sent out at high speed from the back of the engine. This produces a large amount of thrust. The thrust forces the engine forward.

See also JET PROPULSION; THRUST.

PROJECT 49, 59

TURBULENCE (tûr′byə ləns) Turbulence refers to the state of a moving liquid or gas when its movement becomes uneven. For example, a swift-moving river can often be described as turbulent. When turbulence is occurring, the flow of the liquid as a whole may be in a single direction. However, different parts of the liquid are moving at different directions and speeds. Scientists use a factor called Reynold's Number to describe rate of turbulence. Above a certain Reynold's Number, the flow of a liquid ceases to be smooth and becomes turbulent.

Turbulence can also occur in the atmosphere. Sudden updrafts and downdrafts of air caused by heating, cooling, and other factors can cause airplane passengers to have a bumpy ride.

TURNIP The turnip is a biennial vegetable plant belonging to the mustard family, Cruciferae. It belongs to the genus *Brassica* (see BIENNIAL PLANT; VEGETABLE). The upper part of the root swells up with food and this is the part that we eat. Some people also eat the leaves. Turnips grow in northern Europe, the United States, and Canada. They have been a common food in Europe for hundreds of years and in the United States since the 1700s. Turnips are also used to feed livestock.

Turnips are round or oval. They are generally about 4 to 5 in. [10 to 13 cm] in diameter. The flesh is white or yellowish orange in color. Turnips are usually served boiled and mashed. Turnips are high in vitamins A and C.
See also VITAMIN.

TURNSTONE A turnstone is a bird that belongs to the sandpiper family, Scolopacidae. It is up to 10 in. [25 cm] in length. A turnstone has a thin, pointed bill that is slightly curved upward. The bird is found along rocky shores, where it feeds on small water animals. The turnstone was given its name because of its habit of turning over stones in search of food.

There are two species of turnstones. The ruddy turnstone breeds in the Arctic but spends the winter on the coasts of Mexico and the southern United States and as far south as Argentina. It is also found in Europe and many other parts of the world. The black turnstone spends the summer in Alaska and spends the winter along the Pacific coast of Canada, the United States, and Mexico.
See also BIRD.

TURNSTONE

Turnstones are short-billed members of the sandpiper family. The ruddy turnstone (above) is shown catching a small water animal from underneath a rock.

TURNIP

Turnips are root vegetables belonging to the mustard family. They are high in vitamins A and C.

TURQUOISE (tûr′kwoiz′) Turquoise is a soft, blue to green, opaque mineral widely used for jewelry (see MINERAL). (*Opaque* refers to a substance that cannot be seen through.) Chemically, turquoise is a hydrous phosphate of aluminum. This is a compound in which aluminum and phosphorus are combined with water (see COM-POUND). The color of turquoise comes from the presence of small quantities of iron (green) and copper (blue). The most valuable turquoise has a sky blue color. All turquoise fades with time, especially when exposed to much heat or bright light.

Turquoise is found in the Middle East and in the southwestern United States. Because turquoise is in high demand, a large amount of synthetic turquoise is made. Synthetic turquoise is frequently made either entirely from plastic or from turquoise powder mixed with plastic. Inferior grades of green turquoise are also frequently dyed blue to increase their value.

TURTLE *Turtle* is the name for reptiles that have shells (see REPTILE). Most kinds of turtles can pull their head, legs, and tail into their shells for protection.

A turtle's shell is made of bone with a horny covering. It has two main parts. The part of the shell that covers the turtle's back is called the carapace. The plastron is the part that covers the turtle's belly. The bridge is a structure that joins the carapace and plastron on both sides of the body. Some kinds of turtles have a hinged plastron. These turtles can close the plastron tightly against the carapace after withdrawing into their shells. The shells of some turtles are solid brown, dark green, or black. Others are marked with stripes or splotches of green, orange, red, or yellow. Turtles that live only on land are called tortoises (see TORTOISE). Most tortoises have a high, domed shell. Turtles that live in water have a flatter, streamlined shell. Their legs have developed into paddlelike flippers in most species.

The head of most species of turtles is covered by hard scales. Turtles have no teeth. Instead, they have beaks with hard, sharp edges that are used to cut food.

Most turtles eat both animals and plants. Turtles, like other cold-blooded animals, cannot remain

TURTLE

Turtles come in a range of shapes and sizes. Shown here are (1) a matamata and (2) a yellow mud turtle from South America, (3) a spiny soft-shelled turtle from North America, and (4) a green turtle that lives in warm oceans throughout the world.

active in cold weather. Species that live in regions with very cold winters must hibernate. Some species of turtles survive hot, dry periods by going into a state of limited activity. This state is called estivation (see COLD-BLOODED ANIMAL; HIBERNATION).

Turtles hatch from eggs. The eggs are fertilized within the female's body (see EGG; FERTILIZATION). Most kinds of turtles lay their eggs between late spring and late autumn. Some lay eggs more than once during this period. All turtles lay their eggs on land.

There are seven main groups of turtles. They are mud and musk turtles, pond and marsh turtles, sea turtles, side-necked turtles, snapping turtles, soft-shelled turtles, and tortoises. Mud and musk turtles make up a family of twenty-two freshwater species. When disturbed, these turtles give off an unpleasant smelling substance called musk. The common musk turtle has a particularly strong odor. Pond and marsh turtles form the largest family of turtles, with about ninety species. Most pond and marsh turtles live in lakes, ponds, rivers, and streams. A few species spend much of their time on land.

There are about seven species of sea turtles. The turtles in this group are very large. Even the smallest ones, the ridleys, grow to 28 in. [70 cm] in length. A sea turtle called the leatherback or luth may grow to a length of 9 ft. [2.7 m] and weigh about 1,800 lb. [818 kg]. Its shell is over 6 ft. [1.8 m] long.

Side-necked turtles bend their necks sideways when withdrawing their heads. Most turtles pull their heads straight back into their shells. There are about fifty-five species of side-necked turtles.

Snapping turtles are two species of large, flesh-eating freshwater turtles. Their heads are too large to be withdrawn into their shells. They weigh between 50 and 200 lbs. [23 and 92 kg]. Soft-shelled turtles make up a family of twenty-one species. Soft-shelled turtles have a shell covered by smooth skin. Tortoises form a group of about fifty species, all of which are vegetarians.

Many people eat turtle meat and eggs. Some turtle shells are used as ornaments. Several species of turtles have become endangered because of hunting and collecting, pollution, and commercial development of turtle habitats. Rare species of turtles are protected by the governments of some nations.

See also ENDANGERED SPECIES.

TWINS AND TRIPLETS

Twins are two individuals who are born at the same time from the same mother. Triplets are three individuals who are born this way. There have been cases of four or more babies being born at once, but the chance of all of them surviving decreases dramatically with every increase in number. Twins and triplets are the most common examples of multiple births. In the case of twins, each may develop from the same fertilized egg (monozygotic, or identical, twins) or from two different eggs fertilized at the same time (dizygotic, or nonidentical, twins) (see FERTILIZATION). Identical twins are always of the same sex, but nonidentical twins may be of the opposite sex. Triplets and other multiple births are nearly always identical. Psychologists have used identical twins to

TWINS AND TRIPLETS
Monozygotic, or identical, twins develop from the same fertilized egg, which splits in two. They are always the same sex.

study the effects of the environment on human development, because both twins are genetically identical but have different experiences growing up (see GENETICS; PSYCHOLOGY).

TYNDALL EFFECT (tĭn′dl ĭ fĕkt′) The

Tyndall effect refers to the phenomenon that when light hits large particles in the atmosphere, such as dust, it is scattered. This scattering allows light to be visible when it shines through a room.

See also LIGHT; SCATTERING

TYNDALL EFFECT
The Tyndall effect allows sunlight to be visible, as in this woody glade.

TYPHOID FEVER (tī′foid′ fē′vər) Typhoid

fever is an infectious disease caused by a bacterium called *Salmonella typhi* (see BACTERIA; DISEASE). This bacterium (singular of *bacteria*) lives and grows in the waste materials from human bodies. The bacterium is sometimes spread by flies (see FLY). Symptoms of typhoid fever include cough, fever, abdominal discomfort, headache, skin eruption, enlargement of the spleen, and a reduction in the number of white blood cells (see BLOOD; FEVER; SPLEEN).

Contaminated water or milk supplies have caused epidemics of the disease (see EPIDEMIC). A common way of spreading the disease is by a human "carrier." A carrier is a person who does not have the disease but carries the bacteria and therefore can infect others.

Antibiotic drugs are used to treat the disease. Cold sponge baths work to control the fever. In some severe cases, the patient may be given blood transfusions (see ANTIBIOTIC; BLOOD TRANSFUSION).

In preventing the spread of typhoid fever, good hygiene and public sanitation are needed (see HYGIENE). A special vaccine made from the dead bacteria that cause typhoid fever can protect a person for several years.

See also REED, WALTER; VACCINATION.

TYPHUS (tī′fəs) Typhus is any of a group of seri-

ous diseases caused by a microorganism called a rickettsia (see DISEASE; MICROORGANISM; RICKETTSIA). In human beings, the rickettsias damage the walls and linings of blood vessels, causing bleeding and skin rashes. Some rickettsias infect other animals, as well as humans. Typhus diseases can be transmitted from person to person or from an animal to a person by fleas, lice, mites, or ticks (see FLEA; LICE; MITE; TICK).

Epidemic typhus is a serious type of typhus spread by the lice on a human body. This type of typhus has often spread during wars because of crowding and general uncleanliness (see EPIDEMIC). Murine typhus is a milder form of the disease. It is carried by the rat flea. Murine typhus was once a common disease in the southeastern part of the United States.

Doctors use antibiotics to treat typhus. Various insecticides are used to dust people, their clothing, and their belongings to kill the insect carriers of the disease.

See also ANTIBIOTIC; INSECTICIDE.

U

ULNA In human beings, the ulna is one of two long bones in the forearm. The radius is the other bone. The ulna runs from the elbow to the wrist. There are nineteen muscles connected to the ulna and the radius. These muscles move the wrist and fingers. All land vertebrates (animals with backbones) have a bone equivalent to the ulna. *See also* ANATOMY; RADIUS; SKELETON.

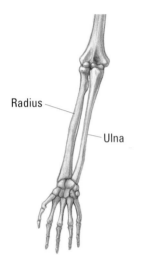

Radius

Ulna

ULNA

The ulna is the longer of the two bones in the forearm. The other bone is called the radius.

ULTRASOUND Sound waves are made by air molecules vibrating back and forth (see SOUND). The number of times they vibrate in a second is called the frequency of the sound wave. Frequency is measured in hertz (see FREQUENCY; HERTZ). The human ear can hear sounds with frequencies as high as 15,000 to 20,000 hertz. Sound above this frequency cannot be heard. It is called ultrasound. Ultrasonics is the study of the production and uses of ultrasound.

One method of producing ultrasound is to use a special crystal called a piezoelectric crystal. The crystal vibrates if the voltage from an alternating current is applied to it (see ALTERNATING CURRENT; VOLT). The frequency at which the crystal vibrates is the same as the frequency at which the voltage alternates. If the voltage is alternating very rapidly, the crystal produces ultrasound (see PIEZOELECTRIC EFFECT).

Ultrasound has many different uses. It is used in sonar equipment on ships and submarines (see SONAR). Ultrasound can be used in industry to measure the thickness of solids. Physicians use ultrasound in different ways. For example, by increasing the intensity of ultrasound, surgeons can use ultrasound instead of a scalpel (surgical knife) to perform delicate operations on the brain or inner ear. In diagnosis, ultrasound may show doctors more than X rays can (see RADIOGRAPHY). Ultrasound imaging, sometimes called sonography, is commonly used to examine fetuses (see PREGNANCY). Ultrasound images can show if there is more than one fetus in the mother's uterus. These images also can show the position and size of a

ULTRASOUND

Ultrasound has various uses in medicine. Here a technician studies an ultrasound image of a person's neck to examine the thyroid gland.

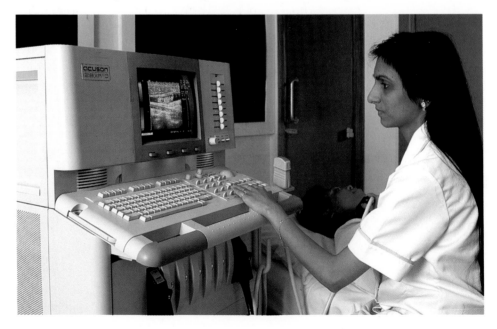

fetus. They can show if there are certain problems with the pregnancy, such as abnormalities in the fetus. Ultrasound imaging also is used to determine how well the heart is working. For example, it can be used to diagnose clogged arteries. Ultrasound imaging can be used to diagnose tumors (abnormal growths), gallstones (pebblelike masses in the gall-bladder), kidney stones (pebblelike masses in the kidneys), and some injuries to the muscles or bones. Ultrasound images usually are read and interpreted by a radiologist, a specially trained doctor (see RADIOLOGY).

In gases, ultrasound causes small particles in the gas to stick together. These larger particles are much easier to remove from the gas than are the smaller particles. This principle is used for removing dust from the air around factories.

ULTRAVIOLET RAY
Ultraviolet rays are an invisible form of light. They lie just beyond the violet end of the visible spectrum. Their frequency is slightly greater than that of violet light (see COLOR; LIGHT; SPECTRUM).

Both visible light and ultraviolet rays are types of electromagnetic radiation (see ELECTROMAGNETIC RADIATION). Different kinds of electromagnetic radiation have different frequencies (see FREQUENCY). Gamma rays have the highest frequency. They are followed by X rays, ultraviolet rays, and visible light. Beyond the red end of visible light are infrared rays and radio waves. This range of different electromagnetic radiations is called the electromagnetic spectrum (see GAMMA RAY; INFRARED RAY; RADIO; X RAY).

The sun produces a large amount of ultraviolet rays. Life could not exist if all these rays reached the earth. Fortunately, most of the ultraviolet rays are absorbed by a gas called ozone that is found in the part of the atmosphere called the stratosphere (see ATMOSPHERE; OZONE LAYER; STRATOSPHERE). Scientists believe that the ozone layer is being destroyed by certain chemical compounds called chlorofluorocarbons (see CHLOROFLUOROCARBONS). This may cause increases in cases of skin cancer around the world. In small amounts, ultraviolet rays can be beneficial. They cause certain chemicals in the skin to change into vitamin D. *See also* VITAMIN.

UMBILICAL CORD
(ŭm bĭl´ĭ kəl kôrd) The umbilical cord attaches the fetus (unborn baby) to the placenta inside the mother's uterus (see EMBRYO; PLACENTA; PREGNANCY; UTERUS). The umbilical cord has two arteries and one vein (see ARTERY; VEIN). The arteries carry the fetus's wastes to the placenta. The vein carries food and oxygen from the mother's blood to the fetus. The physician cuts the umbilical cord after the baby is born. This cutting leaves a permanent scar on the baby's abdomen. The scar is called an umbilicus or navel.

ULTRAVIOLET RAY

The sun produces a large amount of ultraviolet rays. These rays would destroy life on Earth if it were not for a thin layer of the gas ozone in the stratosphere. This ozone layer absorbs most of the ultraviolet rays.

UNCERTAINTY PRINCIPLE In 1927, the German physicist Werner Heisenberg proposed the uncertainty principle. The uncertainty principle states that it is impossible to measure exactly both the position and the velocity of an object at the same time (see VELOCITY). Whenever these measurements are attempted, there is always a certain amount of error. This amount of error is always equal to or greater than a constant quantity. This quantity, 10^{-34} joule-second, is equal to half of Planck's constant divided by pi (3.141592+) (see JOULE; PLANCK, MAX). For most objects, this error is so small that it is not very important. The error becomes important, however, when scientists study atomic or subatomic particles (see ATOM).

The uncertainty principle applies to the measurement of the position and momentum of an object at the same time (see MOMENTUM). It also applies to the measurement of the energy of a moving body and the time it takes to measure the energy.

UNGULATE (ŭng′gyə lĭt) *Ungulate* is the name for any mammal whose toes end in hooves. Sheep, cattle, camels, antelope, horses, deer, and bison are all ungulates. The term *ungulate* comes from the Latin word *ungula,* which means "hoof" (see MAMMAL).

Ungulates are divided into two main groups. Artiodactyls are ungulates with an even number of toes. Most of these animals have two toes on each foot, but the pigs and hippos have four toes. The other group of ungulates, perissodactyls, have an odd number of toes. Horses and rhinoceroses belong to this group. Horses have one toe on each foot. Rhinoceroses have three toes on each foot.

Ungulates are the only mammals that have horns. However, not all ungulates have horns. Most ungulates are herbivores (plant eaters). Pigs and peccaries, however, are omnivores (plant and animal eaters). A peccary is a mammal that is similar to a pig. Many ungulates live on open grasslands.

The ungulate's legs are especially useful for speed. The animals run on the tips of their toes, which in effect gives them longer legs, so they have a longer stride. The lower parts of the legs are usually very light. They can be swung backward and forward with little effort. This allows the animal to run for long periods without getting overly tired. The tough hooves protect the toes from damage on the hard ground.

UNGULATE

The topi (top) is a type of African antelope, and the llama (bottom) is a South American mammal related to the camel. Both animals have hooves and are, therefore, ungulates.

UNIDENTIFIED FLYING OBJECT An unidentified flying object (UFO) is an unknown thing that is seen in the sky and cannot be explained. UFOs are the subject of great controversy. Some people believe that UFOs are spacecraft from other planets. Others believe that UFOs come from natural causes. It is not even certain whether UFOs are material objects in the first place. Many UFO sightings have also been explained as optical illusions caused by the atmosphere (see OPTICAL ILLUSION).

The mention of UFOs can be found throughout history. Many ancient tales mention strange objects in the sky. Most of these ancient sightings might have been connected with lightning or other natural happenings. Since World War II (1939–1945), the number of UFO sightings has increased. Many people have reported seeing "flying saucers." Others claim to have seen objects that looked like cigars. Many UFO reports include sightings of patterns of lights. Scientists and government officials have explained many of these sightings as being airplanes, meteors, planets, smoke, or stars seen under unusual lighting or weather conditions (see METEOR; PLANET; STAR).

Some people claim to have communicated with the occupants of UFOs. Scientists have not paid much attention to most of these claims because of the lack of proof. However, some radio astronomers continue to search for intelligent life beyond Earth. The idea persists that if such life does exist, it may have already visited our planet. *See also* EXOBIOLOGY; RADIO ASTRONOMY.

UNIT In order to measure the size or quantity of something, it has to be compared to a standard quantity. This standard quantity is known as a unit. There are several different systems of units. The system now used by scientists throughout the world is the metric system (see METRIC SYSTEM). The metric system's units of length, mass, and time are the meter, kilogram, and second.

After the units of length, mass, and time have been defined, other quantities can be found. For example, velocity is length divided by time (see VELOCITY). Therefore, velocity is measured in meters per second in the metric system. Momentum is mass times velocity (see MOMENTUM). Momentum is measured in kilogram meters per second in the metric system. For electricity, all systems use the ampere as the main unit of electric current. Other quantities, such as resistance, can be defined by using the ampere and units of length, mass, and time (see AMPERE; RESISTANCE, ELECTRICAL).

Sometimes, units are either too large or too small for a certain branch of science. In these cases, a more practical unit is defined. For example, the meter is much too small for surveyors. Their unit of length is the kilometer. On the other hand, the meter is too large for scientists who study subatomic particles (particles smaller than an atom). They use the unit of length called the nanometer, which is 10^{-9} meters. In the metric system, a multiple or submultiple of the basic unit is always used.

UNIVERSAL JOINT A universal joint is a device that connects two shafts that do not lie in a straight line. It allows the rotational movement (spinning) of one shaft to be passed to the other shaft. For example, in an automobile with rear-wheel drive, the gearbox and the back axle are linked by a shaft called the propeller shaft. There is a universal joint at each end of this shaft. The joint has a wristlike action that sends motion along the propeller shaft. It also allows the propeller shaft to move relative to the gearbox and back axle. The axle is a shaft around which the wheel revolves. This means, for example, that the rear wheels can move up or down when going over bumps independently of the front of the vehicle (see AUTOMOBILE).

The most common kind of universal joint is called the Hooke joint. It is made up of two yokes (clamps) with a cross-shaped link between them. One of the yokes is fitted to the drive shaft and the other to the propeller shaft. These two shafts can then pivot about the link between them. There is a similar arrangement at the other end of the propeller shaft.

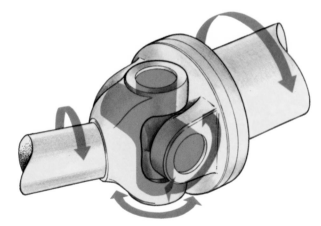

UNIVERSAL JOINT
A universal joint is used to connect two shafts that do not lie in a straight line. The Hooke joint (above) is the simplest type of universal joint. It transmits motion from one shaft to the other. At the same time, it allows the shafts to move about relative to each other.

UNIVERSE

In astronomy, the universe, or cosmos, is every-thing that is known to exist in the form of matter or energy. In a sense, the universe has become larger as more of it has been discovered. Scientific study of the nature, origin, and evolution of the universe is called cosmology (see ASTRONOMY; COSMOLOGY; ENERGY; MATTER).

One of the earliest theories about the universe was put forth by the Greek scientist Ptolemy in the second century A.D. He thought that the

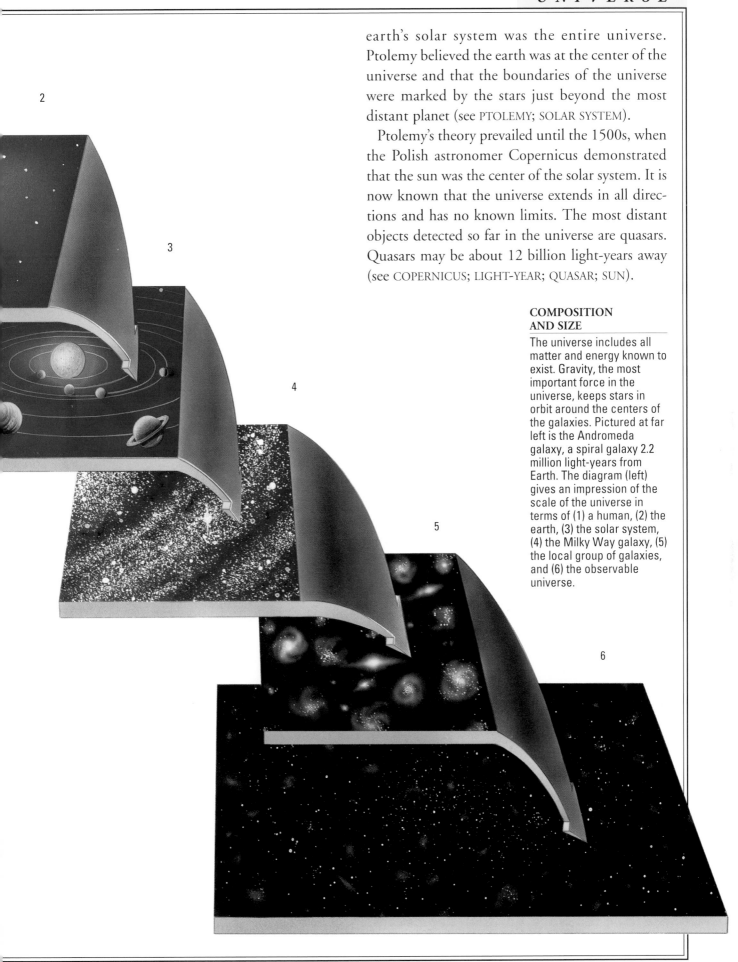

earth's solar system was the entire universe. Ptolemy believed the earth was at the center of the universe and that the boundaries of the universe were marked by the stars just beyond the most distant planet (see PTOLEMY; SOLAR SYSTEM).

Ptolemy's theory prevailed until the 1500s, when the Polish astronomer Copernicus demonstrated that the sun was the center of the solar system. It is now known that the universe extends in all directions and has no known limits. The most distant objects detected so far in the universe are quasars. Quasars may be about 12 billion light-years away (see COPERNICUS; LIGHT-YEAR; QUASAR; SUN).

COMPOSITION AND SIZE

The universe includes all matter and energy known to exist. Gravity, the most important force in the universe, keeps stars in orbit around the centers of the galaxies. Pictured at far left is the Andromeda galaxy, a spiral galaxy 2.2 million light-years from Earth. The diagram (left) gives an impression of the scale of the universe in terms of (1) a human, (2) the earth, (3) the solar system, (4) the Milky Way galaxy, (5) the local group of galaxies, and (6) the observable universe.

The discovery that the earth was not the center of a relatively small universe led to a greatly increased interest in the stars. Astronomers found that the sun is only one of billions of stars orbiting the nucleus (center) of a galaxy called the Milky Way (see GALAXY; MILKY WAY; ORBIT; PLANET; STAR). Using better and larger telescopes, astronomers have discovered that what once appeared to be one star is, in many cases, a cluster of stars or even a galaxy (see TELESCOPE). They have identified thousands of visible galaxies. The galaxies have been found to be arranged into clusters. The clusters are arranged in still larger groups called superclusters.

The matter that makes up the universe is subject to various forces. The most important force in the universe is gravity. Gravity keeps moons in orbit around planets; the planets in orbit around the sun; and stars, such as the sun, in orbit around the centers of galaxies (see GRAVITY).

The most important source of energy in the universe is the conversion of the matter in stars into energy through fusion. Fusion continues within a star until all the star's fuel is used up. Life as we know it on Earth could not exist without the light and heat energy that the sun produces through fusion (see FUSION).

As better and larger telescopes have been developed, astronomers have discovered that all distant galaxies are traveling at high velocities through space (see VELOCITY). The galaxies that are farthest from the Milky Way appear to be traveling away from the earth at nearly the speed of light. This evidence suggests that the universe is expanding. There is also evidence indicating that the original force that first gave the galaxies their motion might have come from the explosion of a black hole (see BLACK HOLE). This very dense body may have once contained all the matter in the universe. However,

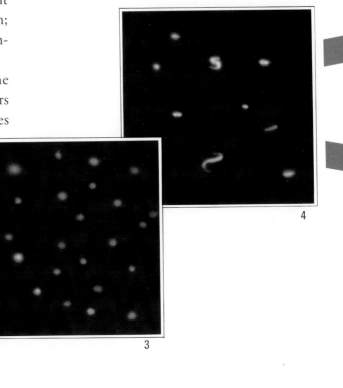

1

2

3

4

FORMATION OF THE UNIVERSE

The formation and early development of the universe is shown on this page. (1) Most astronomers agree that the universe was created by the big bang, the time when time and space began. (2) The universe began to expand. At that time it consisted of a dense, opaque cloud of particles and radiation. (3) As the young universe began to cool, particles condensed to form galaxies, and stars began to shine. (4) About 15,000 million years later, the universe reached its present stage. It is still expanding and is filled with various types of galaxies.

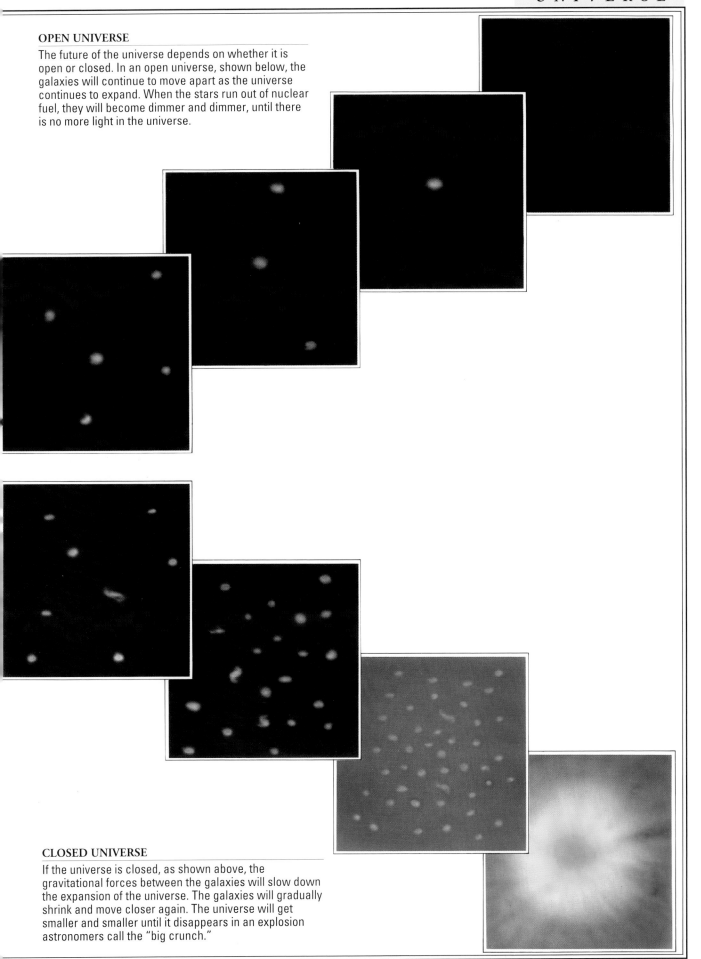

OPEN UNIVERSE

The future of the universe depends on whether it is open or closed. In an open universe, shown below, the galaxies will continue to move apart as the universe continues to expand. When the stars run out of nuclear fuel, they will become dimmer and dimmer, until there is no more light in the universe.

CLOSED UNIVERSE

If the universe is closed, as shown above, the gravitational forces between the galaxies will slow down the expansion of the universe. The galaxies will gradually shrink and move closer again. The universe will get smaller and smaller until it disappears in an explosion astronomers call the "big crunch."

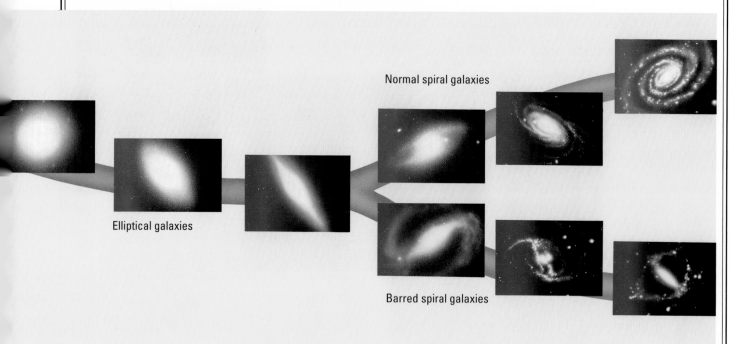

Normal spiral galaxies

Elliptical galaxies

Barred spiral galaxies

TYPES OF GALAXIES

The billions of galaxies in the universe were classified into various types by the U.S. astronomer Edwin Hubble. Elliptical galaxies vary in appearance depending on how flattened they are. Spiral galaxies have a number of arms that curve out from a central bulge (the nucleus). In barred spiral galaxies, the arms curve out from a line or bar of stars that passes through the nucleus.

this theory, called the big bang theory, does not explain where the original body came from (see BIG BANG THEORY).

As new information is discovered, theories about the nature and beginnings of the universe often have to be changed. For example, a theory called the cold-dark-matter theory was developed in the 1980s. This theory suggests that the gravitational force from matter called cold dark matter may have helped create the galaxies. Cold dark matter is believed to be slow-moving subatomic (smaller than an atom) particles. However, in the early 1990s, scientists found that the empty spaces between certain galaxies are so huge that cold dark matter could not possibly have helped create them.

Because the universe is so huge, astronomers cannot observe much of it as it exists today. Instead, they view the light given off by various bodies after

it has traveled through space. For example, astronomers "see" the sun as it was eight minutes earlier. They see the next-nearest star as it was four years earlier. A star a million light-years away from Earth may already have collapsed or exploded. Its light would continue to be visible for a million more years.

Estimates of the age of the universe range from 7 billion years to 20 billion years. These estimates are based on various mathematical models of the universe.

Astronomers and other scientists have established thousands of facts about the forms of matter and energy found in the universe. For example, the development of the spectroscope made it possible to analyze the spectra of radiation given off by heavenly bodies. By analyzing these spectra, scientists can learn such things as the chemical composition and temperature of the heavenly bodies (see ASTRO-PHYSICS; SPECTROSCOPE).

Space telescopes have greatly improved the ability of astronomers and other scientists to describe the structure of the universe. These and other advancements have made accurate mapping of the universe and close study of changes in stars and galaxies possible.

URANIUM (yŏo rā'nē əm) Uranium (U) is a silvery, radioactive, metallic element (see ELEMENT; RADIOACTIVITY). The German chemist Martin Klaproth discovered uranium in 1789. He named it for the planet Uranus. The radioactive properties of uranium were first demonstrated by the French physicist Antoine Henri Becquerel in 1896 (see BECQUEREL, ANTOINE HENRI). The investigations of radioactivity that followed Becquerel's experiments led to the discovery of radium (see RADIUM).

URANIUM—Ores

The chief ores of uranium are pitchblende and carnotite (above), also known as "yellow cake" because of its color.

Natural uranium is a mixture of two main isotopes, uranium-238 and uranium-235 (see ISOTOPE). Most of the uranium found in nature is uranium-238. Uranium occurs naturally in the ore pitchblende (see PITCHBLENDE). It is also found in many other minerals.

The most important use for uranium is as a fuel for nuclear reactors (see NUCLEAR ENERGY). For a long time, uranium compounds were used to color glass and ceramics (see COMPOUND). Today, this process is recognized as dangerous because uranium compounds are both highly toxic (poisonous) and radioactive.

All isotopes of uranium are radioactive. They decay to form other elements. The longest-lived isotope is uranium-238. It has a half-life of 4,510 million years. The half-life of uranium-235 is 710 million years (see HALF-LIFE). Uranium's atomic number is 92, and its relative atomic mass is 238.03. It melts at 2,070°F [1,132°C] and boils at 6,904°F [3,818°C]. The relative density of uranium is 19.0. Uranium is the heaviest natural element.

See also RELATIVE DENSITY.

Slow neutron

Uranium-235

Uranium-236

Fission fragment

Neutrons

Fission fragment

U-235

U-235

U-235

URANIUM—Fission

Uranium-235 is an isotope of uranium that undergoes fission. This is a reaction in which absorption of a neutron by the nucleus of a uranium-235 atom causes it to split into two smaller atoms, called fission fragments. The reaction releases large amounts of heat energy as well as two or three more neutrons, which go on to produce more fission in a chain reaction.

URANUS

Uranus (yo͝or′ə nəs) is the third largest planet in the solar system (see PLANET; SOLAR SYSTEM). It is located seventh in order from the sun. The British astronomer Sir William Herschel discovered Uranus in 1781 with a telescope he made himself (see HERSCHEL, SIR WILLIAM).

Uranus has a diameter of about 32,500 mi. [52,200 km]. The planet lies an average of 1,780,000,000 mi. [2,870,000,000 km] from the sun. It takes Uranus about eighty-four years to make a complete trip around the sun. Uranus makes one complete spin on its axis (an imaginary line running through its center) every seventeen hours. Uranus's axis is unusual because it lies in almost exactly the same plane as the planet's orbit. This means that the North and South poles of Uranus are practically in line with the equators of the other planets. An equator is an imaginary line running around the middle of a planet. As Uranus revolves around the sun every eighty-four years, its axis always points in the same direction. This means that one of Uranus's poles is in sunlight for forty-two years, while the other pole is in darkness. Then, during the next forty-two years, the conditions are switched.

Uranus is the most distant planet from the earth that can be seen by the naked eye. Astronomers know little about the planet's physical characteristics. They do know that nearly all of Uranus's upper atmosphere is made of helium and hydrogen with small amounts of methane. Scientists believe that the planet's lower atmosphere is made of ammonia, methane, and water vapor. The methane gives the planet its bluish green color. The average temperature on the surface of Uranus is estimated to be -357°F [-216°C].

Uranus has fifteen natural satellites, or moons (see SATELLITE). The moons vary greatly in size. Some are only about 10 mi. [16 km] in diameter. Others are about 988 mi. [1,590 km] in diameter. One of Uranus's moons, Miranda, is very unusual. Its landforms, such as craters, flat areas, and giant canyons, are arranged in a jumbled manner. Many scientists think that the shape of Miranda's landscape was formed by a collision with another heavenly body. The collision broke Miranda apart. Later, gravity brought the pieces back together into the jumbled mass it is today (see GRAVITY). Also orbiting Uranus are ten rings. Scientists have known of nine of the rings since 1977. The *Voyager 2* space probe discovered another faint ring in 1986.

See also SPACE EXPLORATION.

STRUCTURE OF URANUS

Uranus has an iron-silicate core, surrounded by a mantle composed of frozen ammonia, methane, and water (ice). It has a thick atmosphere of ammonia, methane, and water vapor near the surface, with helium and hydrogen in the upper atmosphere.

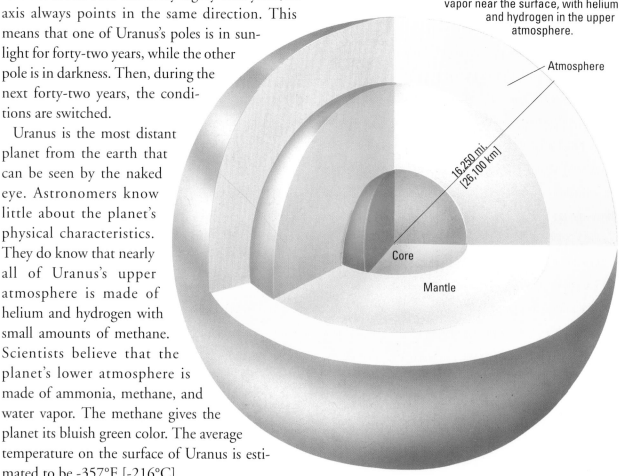

Atmosphere

16,250 mi. [26,100 km]

Core

Mantle

UREA (yŏŏ rē′ə) Urea is a nitrogen-containing organic compound. An organic compound contains the element carbon (see COMPOUND). The chemical formula for urea is H_2NCONH_2. Urea is a waste product that results when proteins are metabolized (used) in mammals and some fish (see METABOLISM). Urea is formed in the liver and is excreted by the kidneys as part of urine (see EXCRETION; URINE).

Urea was first made artificially in 1828 by the German chemist Friedrich Wohler. It was the first naturally occurring organic compound to be made in the laboratory. This discovery is considered to be the birth of synthetic (human-made) organic chemistry.

Commercially, urea is prepared from ammonia and carbon dioxide. Because it contains so much nitrogen, urea is used in many fertilizers (see FERTILIZER). It is also added to animal feed and is used in making enamels, explosives, permanent-press fabrics, plastics, and waterproof paper. Urea is used in the drug industry to make barbiturates. Urea is sometimes called carbamide.

See also BARBITURATE.

URETER (yŏŏr′ĭ tər) In mammals, birds, and reptiles, the ureter is a tube that carries urine from each kidney to a storage organ called the urinary bladder, usually referred to simply as the bladder.

See also EXCRETION; KIDNEY; URINE.

URETHRA (yŏŏ rē′ thrə) In most mammals, the urethra is a tube in the body that carries urine from the urinary bladder to the outside of the body. In females, it is totally separate from the reproductive system. In males, however, the vas deferens connects with the urethra and both sperm and urine leave through the same opening.

See also EXCRETION; REPRODUCTIVE SYSTEM; URINE.

UREY, HAROLD CLAYTON (1893–1981) (yŏŏr′ ē, hăr′ əld klāt′n) Harold Urey was an American chemist. He was born in Walkerton, Indiana, and studied at the University of Montana. In 1931, Urey began to try to obtain deuterium, an isotope of hydrogen. Deuterium is sometimes called heavy hydrogen (see HYDROGEN; ISOTOPE). Other scientists believed this isotope existed, but it had not actually been discovered yet. Urey decided to try to obtain deuterium by evaporating ordinary hydrogen. He succeeded in evaporating enough ordinary hydrogen to be able to measure the heavy hydrogen that was left. Urey received the Nobel Prize for chemistry in 1934 for this discovery.

Urey continued to work on isotopes. He discovered how to separate uranium isotopes during World War II (1939–1945) (see URANIUM). Later, Urey became worried about the use of his own and other discoveries in military weapons. He gave up work on what he thought would be used as weapons and devoted his research to geology. He helped date fossils and developed theories of the formation of the planets (see DATING; FOSSIL). Urey even proposed what the atmosphere of the earth might have been like when life began.

URINE (yŏŏr′ĭn) Urine is a liquid waste product of the body that the kidneys manufacture. The urine of a healthy person is yellowish in color and slightly acidic (see ACID; KIDNEY). It is heavier than water and has an average relative density of 1.022 (see RELATIVE DENSITY). Urine is made up of creatinine, urea, uric acid, water, and inorganic salts. These salts include ammonium, calcium, magnesium, potassium, and sodium salts.

The kidneys remove wastes and water from the blood and body tissues. The substances pass to the bladder and are expelled from the body as urine. Urine is produced in larger quantities when a person drinks large amounts of liquid. When a person perspires, he or she produces less urine.

The condition of urine often explains something about a person's health. Too much glucose (sugar) in the urine is a symptom of diabetes. Blood in the urine can mean that the kidneys have been damaged.

See also DIABETES; EXCRETION; UREA.

UTERUS (yŏŏ′tər əs) The uterus, or womb, is a hollow organ that is part of the female reproductive system. It is shaped like an upside-down pear. Its lowest section, the cervix, is a necklike opening to the vagina, or birth canal. In its upper section are the openings to the two fallopian tubes (see ORGAN; REPRODUCTIVE SYSTEM).

The uterus is made of three layers of muscles that are intertwined with many fibers and blood vessels. The inside of the uterus is lined with a moist mucous membrane called the endometrium (see MUCOUS MEMBRANE). The thickness of the endometrium changes during the menstrual cycle (see MENSTRUAL CYCLE). It is thickest at ovulation, when the egg is released from an ovary. In preparation for a fertilized egg, the endometrium swells with added blood, proteins, glucose (sugar), and minerals. If the egg is fertilized, it implants in the endometrium and begins developing (see FERTIL-IZATION; IMPLANTATION). Development continues in the uterus until the baby is born, about nine months later (see PREGNANCY). If the egg is not fertilized, it and the outer lining of the endometrium are released through the vagina during menstrual bleeding.

See also REPRODUCTION.

V

VACCINATION (văk′sə nā′shən) Vaccination is the placement of dead or weakened pathogens (disease-causing organisms) into the body. This causes the body to develop resistance to the disease caused by the pathogen. The material, which is usually injected, is called a vaccine (see INFECTION). The term *vaccination* comes from the Latin word *vacca*, meaning "cow." Edward Jenner, the first person to use and encourage vaccination, used cowpox germs to give resistance to smallpox (see DISEASE; IMMUNITY; INFECTION; JENNER, EDWARD; SMALLPOX).

A vaccine causes cells of the immune system to produce substances called antibodies. Antibodies fight antigens, which include bacteria and viruses (see ANTIBODY; BACTERIA; VIRUS). Vaccines must be strong enough to cause the body to develop resistance to a disease. However, they must be weak enough that they do not cause serious illness.

Effective vaccines have been developed against many diseases, such as cholera, measles, mumps, poliomyelitis, rabies, typhoid fever, and smallpox.

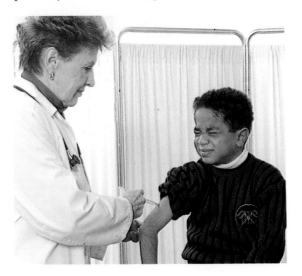

VACCINATION

When people are vaccinated, dead or weakened disease-causing organisms are introduced into their bodies. This causes the body to develop resistance to that particular disease.

VACUOLE (văk′yoo ōl′) A vacuole is usually a fluid-filled space in a cell. It is enclosed by a membrane that separates it from the surrounding cytoplasm. Many, though not all, cells have vacuoles. Animal cells have only very small vacuoles, but some plant cells contain a vacuole occupying almost all of the cell. In protozoans, food vacuoles digest food. Contractile vacuoles squirt out wastes and excess water. Some vacuoles, particularly in microorganisms, contain gases instead of fluids.

See also CELL; MEMBRANE; MICROORGANISM; PROTOZOA.

VACUUM A vacuum is a space that contains no matter. There is no such thing as a complete vacuum, however. Scientists have not yet developed a way to remove all the air molecules from a space. The easiest way to produce a vacuum is to remove the air from inside a strong container. The container has to be strong or it will collapse when the air is removed. The air can be removed by using a device called a vacuum pump.

A vacuum has several important properties. One of these properties is that it will not conduct heat. This property is used in the Dewar flask (see DEWAR

FLASK). A Dewar flask is used for keeping substances at a constant temperature. It is a bottle-shaped container that contains an inner container made of glass. Between the walls of the two containers there is a vacuum. This vacuum prevents any heat loss by conduction or convection. However, the Dewar flask does lose a small amount of heat by radiation. This is because heat radiation can travel through a vacuum (see HEAT).

Sound will not travel in a vacuum because sound is transmitted, or sent, by matter. For example, on the moon there is very little atmosphere, so astronauts must use radios to talk to one another. They cannot hear one another by speaking normally (see SOUND).

A vacuum is measured by the pressure of the gases in it. The lower the pressure, the more perfect the vacuum. The unit often used to measure a vacuum is the metric system unit of pressure called the pascal. *See also* PRESSURE. **PROJECT 57**

VACUUM TUBE A vacuum tube is a device used in some types of electronic equipment. Before the invention of transistors, vacuum tubes were used in many types of electrical equipment (see ELECTRONICS; TRANSISTOR). However, transistors have largely replaced vacuum tubes because they are smaller, lighter, and more dependable and give off less heat. Vacuum tubes are still used in certain

VACUUM TUBE
This vacuum tube is a type of triode used for strengthening electrical current.

high-power amplifiers (see AMPLIFIER).

A vacuum tube is a container that is usually made of glass. The air is pumped from the tube, and the tube is then sealed to leave a vacuum inside (see VACUUM). A vacuum tube also contains at least two electrodes. These create the electric current and allow it to enter or leave. An electric current is a flow of electric charges, or electrons, through a wire (see CURRENT, ELECTRIC; ELECTRODE; ELECTRON). The electrodes are connected to the outside by wires that pass through the glass. Vacuum tubes may also contain electrodes that are grids. They control the amount of electrons flowing through the tube.

The simplest vacuum tube is the diode. The diode allows the current to pass in only one direction. One electrode in a diode, called the cathode, gives out electrons when it is heated. The cathode is heated when a current is passed through it. The other electrode in a diode is called the anode. The electrons that the cathode gives out are attracted to the anode. In a diode, the electrons can flow only from the cathode to the anode. They cannot flow in the opposite direction. Diodes act as rectifiers because they change alternating current into a direct current (see ALTERNATING CURRENT; DIRECT CURRENT; RECTIFIER).

Another type of vacuum tube that contains a grid as well as a cathode and an anode is called the triode. The grid is placed between the anode and the cathode. The grid produces a change in the current flowing through the tube. The change it produces is to amplify (strengthen) the current.

VALENCE (vā′ləns) Valence is the number of chemical bonds that the atoms of an element can form. When atoms bond together, they form molecules (see ATOM; ELEMENT; MOLECULE). For example, hydrogen has a valence of one. Therefore, its atoms each have one bond for combining with other atoms. Carbon has a valence of four and can form four bonds. Therefore, four atoms of hydrogen can combine with one atom of carbon to form a compound called methane. Its chemical formula, CH_4, shows that each molecule of methane contains one atom of carbon and four atoms of hydrogen (see COMPOUND).

Many elements have more than one valence. For example, iron can have a valence of either two or three. Chlorine has a valence of one. Iron and chlorine can form two different compounds. One is called ferrous chloride. Its formula is $FeCl_2$. In this compound, iron has a valence of two. The other compound is called ferric chloride. Its formula is $FeCl_3$. Here, iron has a valence of three.

A group of atoms may also have a valence. Such a group is called a radical (see RADICAL). An example is the sulfate radical. The sulfate radical has the formula SO_4 and has a valence of two. With iron, it forms either iron (II) sulfate ($FeSO_4$) or iron (III) sulfate ($Fe_2(SO_4)_3$). An atom or radical with a valence of one is said to be univalent. An atom or radical with a valence of two is said to be divalent. A trivalent atom or radical has a valence of three.

Sometimes, the valence of an element can be figured from the formulas of its compounds. For example, calcium forms the compound calcium sulfate, $CaSO_4$. The valence of the sulfate radical is two. Therefore, it follows that the valence of calcium is also two because one atom of calcium combines with one sulfate radical. However, this way of figuring valence does not always work. Carbon and hydrogen form a compound called ethane (see ETHANE). Its formula is C_2H_6. Because hydrogen has a valence of one, it seems as though carbon must have a valence of three in ethane. However, the actual arrangement of the atoms in a molecule of ethane is like this:

$$\begin{array}{ccc} & H & H \\ & | & | \\ H- & C- & C-H \\ & | & | \\ & H & H \end{array}$$

The carbon atom still has four bonds and, therefore, has a valence of four.

VAMPIRE BAT The vampire bat is a small bat that bites warm-blooded animals, such as cattle and fowl, and then licks the blood from the wound. Vampire bats belong to the family Desmodontidae. Vampire bats live in Central and South America (see BAT; WARM-BLOODED ANIMAL).

The common vampire bat is a reddish brown animal about 3 in. [8 cm] long. It has very sharp, triangular front teeth. Vampire bats sometimes attack persons who are sleeping. The actual bite of a vampire bat is not serious and heals quickly. Also, the bat takes only a small amount of blood. However, many vampire bats carry rabies, a disease that is fatal if not treated in time (see RABIES). Cattle and other large animals are attacked more often by vampire bats than humans are. Cattle living in areas where there are vampire bats are often vaccinated against rabies.

See also VACCINATION.

VAMPIRE BAT

Vampire bats bite warm-blooded prey and then use the blood produced by the wound as food. The actual bite is not serious, but vampire bats may carry and spread the disease rabies.

VAN ALLEN, JAMES ALFRED (1914–) James Van Allen is an American physicist. He was born in Mount Pleasant, Iowa. During World War II (1939–1945), Van Allen was one of the many scientists working on military matters. After the war, Van Allen used military rockets for investigating cosmic rays. Cosmic rays are streams of tiny particles that enter the earth's atmosphere from space (see COSMIC RAYS).

In 1958, Van Allen discovered the first of two zones of electrically charged particles that surround the earth. These zones are now referred to as the Van Allen belts. The earth's magnetic field is responsible for trapping these particles.

See also MAGNETIC FIELD; MAGNETISM; VAN ALLEN BELTS.

VAN ALLEN BELTS

The Van Allen belts are two zones of electrically charged particles that surround the earth like irregularly shaped doughnuts. They are named for James Van Allen, an American scientist, who discovered them in 1958 (see VAN ALLEN, JAMES ALFRED). The inner belt extends from about 600 to 3,000 mi. [1,000 to 5,000 km] above the earth. The outer belt extends from about 9,300 to 15,500 mi. [15,000 to 25,000 km] above the earth.

The inner belt, which has the most energy, consists of electrons and protons (see ELECTRON; ENERGY; PROTON). The outer belt contains mostly electrons. The belts acquire new particles from the solar wind and solar flares.

See also SOLAR WIND; SUN.

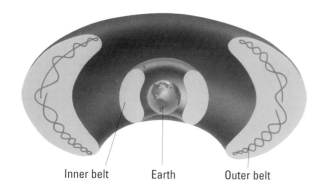

Inner belt   Earth   Outer belt

VAN ALLEN BELTS

The Van Allen belts are two doughnut-shaped zones of electrically charged particles that surround the earth.

VAN DE GRAAFF GENERATOR

A Van de Graaff generator is a machine that is used for producing very high voltages (see GENERATOR; VOLT). It contains a moving belt of insulating material that runs around two pulleys, one above the other. Near the bottom pulley are a number of fine needles with their points close to the belt. These needles are connected to a potential of 10,000 to 50,000 volts. The moving belt picks up a charge from the needles and carries it to the top of the generator. The upper

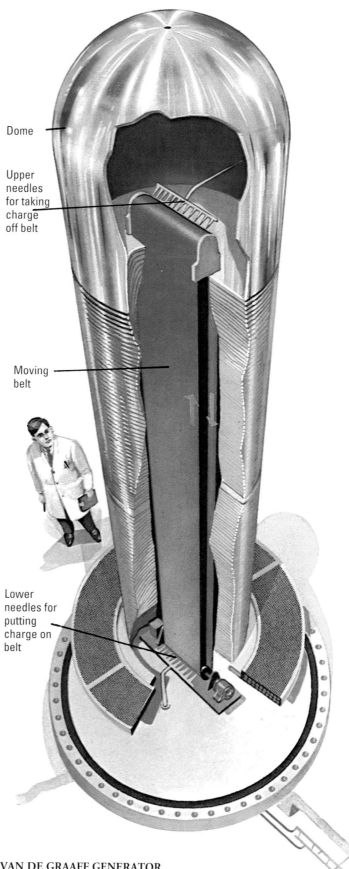

Dome

Upper needles for taking charge off belt

Moving belt

Lower needles for putting charge on belt

VAN DE GRAAFF GENERATOR

A Van de Graaff generator is used for producing very high voltages. In the diagram (above), the exterior is partly cut away to reveal the interior.

pulley is at the center of a large metal dome. More needles around the upper pulley collect the charge from the belt. These needles are connected to the dome. The charges flow from the needles to the dome. As the charge builds up, a potential difference of several million volts is produced between the dome and the outside (see POTENTIAL).

The dome must be well insulated, and the air around it must be dry (see INSULATION). Because water conducts electricity, moisture in the air could cause the dome to discharge, or emit its electrical charges. Walls or other objects near the dome could also discharge the generator. When a generator discharges, the effect is like a flash of lightning.

Modern generators are enclosed in a steel tank containing gas at a pressure of about 20 to 30 atmospheres (see ATMOSPHERE (UNIT)). This helps reduce the chance of an accidental discharge. Van de Graaff generators are used by scientists to study nuclear forces.
See also FORCE.

VAN DER WAALS, JOHANNES (1837–1923)
Johannes van der Waals was a Dutch physicist. He was born at Leiden, a city in the Netherlands, and studied at the university there. He was interested in the physics of gases and liquids. Van der Waals knew of the work of Robert Boyle and Jacques Alexander Charles and set out to find out why their equations did not exactly match the way gases and liquids behave (see BOYLE'S LAW; CHARLES'S LAW). He determined that the size of molecules, together with forces between molecules, affect their behavior. Even though gas molecules are extremely small, each molecule of a particular gas is a different size. This means that the molecules of different gases behave differently. The forces between molecules in a gas are called van der Waals forces. In 1910, van der Waals was awarded the Nobel Prize for physics for this work.
See also GAS; LIQUID; MOLECULE; VAN DER WAALS FORCES.

VAN DER WAALS FORCES
Van der Waals forces are forces that act between atoms or molecules. They are named after the Dutch physicist, Johannes van der Waals. In 1873, he produced an equation that related the pressure and temperature of a gas to its volume. He assumed that the pressure would be a little larger than previous equations had predicted, because of forces of attraction between the molecules of the gas. His equation was more accurate than earlier equations, and scientists realized that these forces did exist. Van der Waals forces are very weak. They act only when atoms or molecules are close together.
See also FORCE; GAS; MOLECULE; PRESSURE; TEMPERATURE; VAN DER WAALS, JOHANNES; VOLUME.

VAPOR
A vapor is a gas produced by heating a solid or a liquid that can return to its liquid or solid state under high pressure at ordinary temperatures. Most gases, on the other hand, need high pressure and cool temperatures to return to their liquid or solid state.
See also GAS; LIQUID; PRESSURE; TEMPERATURE; VAPOR PRESSURE.

PROJECT 23

VAPOR PRESSURE
Vapor pressure is the pressure produced by vapor molecules as they escape from a liquid or solid during evaporation. If the vapor pressure is increased, evaporation increases (see EVAPORATION; LIQUID; MOLECULE; SOLID; VAPOR). Vapor pressure can be increased by increasing the temperature. Eventually, at a certain temperature, the vapor pressure of the liquid is equal to the pressure of the atmosphere. At this temperature, the liquid boils (see ATMOSPHERE; BOILING AND BOILING POINT; TEMPERATURE). If the atmospheric pressure increases or decreases, the boiling point of the liquid increases or decreases. For example, at high altitudes, atmospheric pressure is less than it is at sea level. At the higher altitudes, the boiling point of water is less than the 212°F [100°C] it is at sea level.

VARIABLE STAR
A variable star is a star whose light changes from bright to dim to bright again. There are several causes of such changes in the brightness of stars (see STAR).

Some stars expand (grow larger) and contract (grow smaller) at regular intervals. These stars are

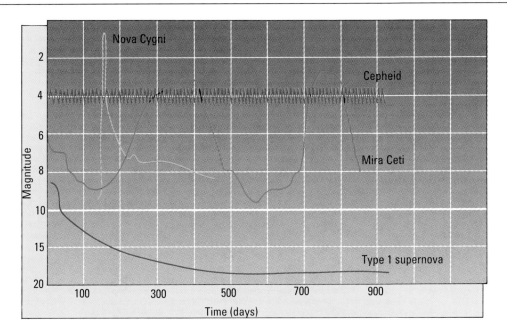

There are various types of variable stars. In all cases, the magnitude of the star (the amount of light it produces) varies over a period of time (left). A nova, such as Nova Cygni or a Type 1 supernova, produces one outburst of light and then fades. A Cepheid variable produces regular pulses of light, from one day to one hundred days apart. A Mira variable produces regular pulses of light also, but its periods are longer. For example, the Mira Ceti's pulses are up to two years apart.

called pulsating variables. The time between expansions is known as the star's period. The North Star is a pulsating variable with a period of about four days. Any variable star with a period of less than fifty days is called a short-period variable. Some pulsating variables have periods longer than one hundred days. These are called long-period variables. Irregular variables have no set period.

Cepheid variables are an important type of pulsating variable. They have periods ranging from about one day to one hundred days. The longer the period of a Cepheid variable, the greater is the star's average brightness. This fact is used to measure the distance to galaxies containing Cepheid variables. Mira variables have much longer periods of several hundred days.

Some stars have great explosions that increase their brightness by millions of times. These are called exploding stars, or novae (see NOVA). The increased brightness may last for days, weeks, or even years. Eventually, the star returns to its previous brilliance. Extremely bright exploding stars are called supernovae (see SUPERNOVA).

Binary stars are two stars that revolve around each other. One of them occasionally blocks the light of the other. Such a double star is called an eclipsing binary. Eclipsing binaries are not considered true variables because internal processes of these stars are not responsible for their variation of light.

VARIATION Variations are the differences in appearance or behavior between members of a particular plant or animal species (see SPECIES). Variations are largely the result of changes in the genes or chromosomes of the organisms (see CHROMOSOME; GENE). There are always some slight differences between individuals because they do not all receive the same combination of genes from their parents. Bigger variations can occur as a result of mutations, which are accidental changes in the make-up of individual genes or chromosomes (see MUTATION).

Variations are the raw materials of evolution (see EVOLUTION). Useful variations persist because of natural selection, and populations possessing them become better suited to their environment (see NATURAL SELECTION). An organism that has undergone a harmful or useless mutation usually dies before it can pass on the mutated gene, although mutations can reappear.
See also GENETICS.

VARNISH Varnish is a transparent liquid (one that can be seen through) that is often applied to materials, such as wood or metal, for protection. Varnish protects objects chiefly from air and moisture. It is also used for decorative purposes. After being brushed or sprayed onto the surface of an object, the varnish dries, leaving behind a hard and often glossy film.

A varnish that is clear protects the surface of wood. It also allows the natural grain of the wood to show through. Varnish stains contain dyes. These dyes change the color of the wood, but they also bring out the grain of the wood. Varnishes used on metal are frequently called lacquers (see LAC-QUER). In certain cases, varnish is used to protect insulating wires and paper from moisture. Varnishes can be baked on. Baking improves the wearing ability of the object.

There are two main kinds of varnish—spirit and oleoresinous. Spirit varnishes are made of resins (see RESIN). Shellac is a common spirit varnish (see SHELLAC). Oleoresinous varnishes are mixtures of resins and drying oils that are heated and dissolved in turpentine or petroleum products. Oleoresinous varnishes can withstand outdoor conditions well.

VASCULAR PLANT (văs'kyə lər plănt)
Vascular plants have a special transport system in their roots, stems, and leaves. This vascular system is made of tissues called xylem and phloem (see PHLOEM; XYLEM). Xylem carries water and dissolved minerals from where they are absorbed (roots) to where they are used in photosynthesis (leaves). Phloem carries dissolved food and other substances from where they are produced (leaves) to all other parts of the plant. In addition to its

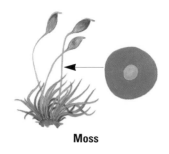

Moss

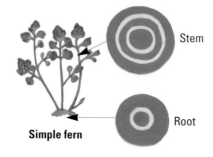

Simple fern

Stem

Root

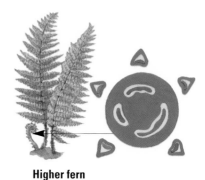

Higher fern

VASCULAR PLANT

Some nonvascular plants, such as mosses, have a central core of differentiated cells, but the function of these cells is not known. The simplest vascular structure is found in the roots of simple ferns, where a central core of xylem (red) is surrounded by a ring of phloem (yellow). In the stems of these ferns, the xylem forms a ring, with phloem both inside and outside. Where leaves branch off, this ring is broken, and in the most advanced ferns, the vascular tissue appears as a number of bundles whose structure is the same as in the simple fern. In angiosperms, the vascular tissues are broken up into bundles. The arrangements of these bundles are different in monocotyledons and dicotyledons.

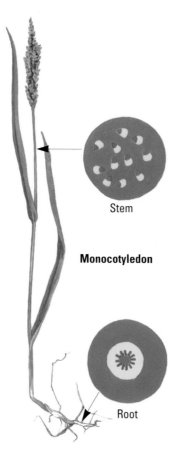

Stem

Monocotyledon

Root

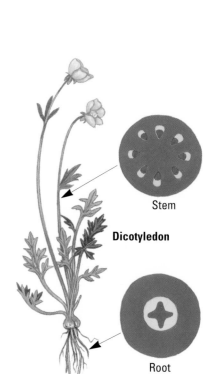

Stem

Dicotyledon

Root

transport function, the vascular system gives the plant strength and support.

The vascular plants include the angiosperms, club mosses, ferns, gymnosperms, and horsetails. Most of these plants live on land. They are classified in various divisions of the plant kingdom. *See also* PLANT KINGDOM.

VECTOR QUANTITY

A vector quantity is one that has both magnitude (size) and direction. An example of a vector quantity is velocity. Velocity is speed in a certain direction. The speed is the magnitude of the force (see VELOCITY). Two airplanes flying toward each other can have the same speed. However, their velocities are different because they are traveling in opposite directions. However, three planes flying in formation at the same speed have the same velocity.

A vector quantity can be shown by a line. The length of the line stands for the magnitude. An arrowhead is placed on the line to show direction. For example, two forces, F1 and F2, can be shown as follows:

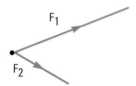

These two forces are acting at a single point, shown by a black dot. If they are both acting on one body, then the body moves as if a single force were acting upon it. This single force is a combination of the two forces. It is called the resultant of the two forces. The resultant is found by adding the two vector quantities together. Because vector quantities have direction, they cannot be added as though they were numbers. To add two vector quantities, they must be placed so that the head of one is touching the tail of the other. Then a line is drawn connecting the two free ends. This line is

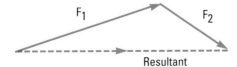

Resultant

the resultant vector quantity.

The addition of vector quantities is very important in deciding the course of an aircraft. Suppose an aircraft is scheduled to fly in a certain direction so that it gets from town A to town B. However, there is also a wind blowing at right angles to this direction. The aircraft has to head into the wind slightly to make up for the force of the wind. Therefore, the aircraft actually heads toward point C on its way to town B.

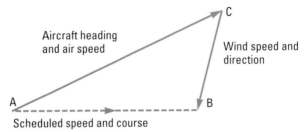

Suppose there are three forces acting on a body. If, when the vector quantities are added, the head or tail of a line is always connected to the head or tail of another line, there is no resultant force. The forces balance each other out. The body is said to be in equilibrium.

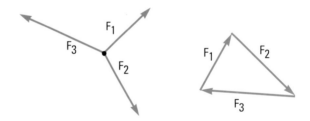

VEGETABLE

A vegetable is the edible part of a herbaceous plant (see HERBACEOUS PLANT). A vegetable can be a root, stem, leaf, or other part of certain plants, such as a bulb, flower, or tuber.

Root vegetables include carrots and turnips. Potatoes are also classed as root vegetables, although they are really tubers (see TUBER). Edible stems include asparagus and celery. Leaf vegetables, often called green vegetables, include lettuce, spinach, and numerous forms of cabbage. Broccoli and cauliflower are also varieties of cabbage, but we eat the flower buds of these vegetables. Garlic and onions are bulbs (see BULB AND CORM).

Confusion often arises in determining whether a

food is a fruit or a vegetable. Foods with seeds, such as beans, corn, cucumbers, peas, and tomatoes, are really fruits, even though most people think of them as vegetables (see FRUIT).

Vegetables are an important part of a balanced diet. They are usually good sources of vitamins, minerals, and fiber. They also provide valuable proteins and energy-giving carbohydrates.

See also DIET; FOOD; NUTRITION.

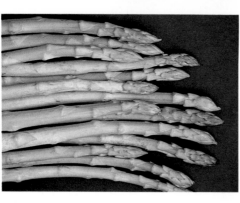

VEGETABLE

Different vegetables (left) come from different types of plants. Lettuce (top) is a leaf vegetable. Carrots (below) are root vegetables. Potatoes (below center), which are tubers, are among the most widely eaten vegetables. Asparagus (bottom left) is an edible stem.

VEGETATIVE PROPAGATION (věj'ĭ tā'tĭv prŏp'ə gā' shən)

Vegetative propagation is the production of a complete new plant from part of an existing plant without the use of seeds. The part of the plant used in vegetative propagation may be the stem, leaf, or root. The ability to grow new body parts to replace lost or damaged ones is called regeneration. Vegetative propagation is a type of asexual reproduction (see ASEXUAL REPRODUCTION; LEAF; REGENERATION; ROOT; STEM).

Many plants, such as the strawberry, have stems that grow along the surface of the ground. These stems are called runners, or stolons. The runners produce roots that grow into the ground. New leaves appear and, when the runners are cut or die away, several new plants are left. Many other plants, including some grasses, have underground stems called rhizomes. These propagate in the same way as runners (see RHIZOME).

Some plants produce tiny buds that fall off and begin to grow. These buds, called bulbils, have a better chance of growing than do seeds. In some plants, the bulbils even start to grow before they fall from the parents.

Artificial vegetative propagation

Farmers, gardeners, and florists often use vegetative propagation to produce many plants that are exactly the same as the original, parent plant. The major artificial methods are cutting, grafting, budding and layering.

In cutting, a small part (usually a stem) is cut from a growing plant and placed in water or moist

VEGETATIVE PROPAGATION

This agricultural worker (left) is grafting (attaching) a new stem onto a mango. A strawberry plant (above) reproduces using vegetative propagation by sending out runners, which take root some distance from the parent plant.

soil. In most cases, the cutting develops roots and grows into a complete plant. In another type of cutting, a bud is removed and planted. For example, a potato can be cut into several pieces, each of which has an eye (bud). If these pieces are planted, each will grow into a new potato plant.

Grafting is similar to cutting, except the cut plant part is grafted, or attached, onto another plant. The cutting, or plant part, is called a scion, and the rooted plant to which it is attached is called a stock. The vascular tissues must be lined up so that they will grow together (see VASCULAR PLANT). The stock becomes the new plant's roots. The scion becomes the upper part, and the flowers and fruits are all formed by the scion. Many kinds of apples are grown this way. By grafting more than one variety on to a single stock, it is possible to grow several kinds of apples on one tree.

Budding is much like grafting. A bud is cut from one plant and inserted into the stem of another plant. As long as their cambiums are in contact, the bud will grow (see CAMBIUM). In this way, it is possible to have one plant with several kinds of flowers or fruits.

There are two types of layering: mound and aerial. In mound layering, soil is piled up around the branches or stem of a plant. Roots then grow from the branch or stem into the soil. These rooted parts can be cut off and planted. In aerial layering, a slice is made into a stem or branch, near a bud. The whole area is then packed with moss and covered with waterproof wrapping. Roots grow into the moss. This part can then be cut off and planted.

Advantages of vegetative propagation

The plants produced by vegetative propagation have exactly the same features as the parent plant. Certain desired characteristics of the parent plant, such as seedless fruits and resistance to disease, can thus be passed on through vegetative propagation. It is therefore possible to raise many identical plants. Growing plants from seeds is much slower and does not guarantee that all the plants will have the desired features.

See also BREEDING.

VEIN (vān) A vein is a blood vessel that carries blood toward the heart. Blood circulates through the body in veins as well as through two other kinds of blood vessels, called arteries and capillaries. Veins are thinner and less muscular than arteries. Capillaries are the smallest of the three kinds of blood vessels; they connect the arteries and veins (see ARTERY; CAPILLARY). Arteries carry blood from the heart to the various parts of the body. Veins return the blood after it has nourished the tissues and taken on waste products. Most of the returning blood contains little oxygen and is therefore purplish red in color. Blood from the pulmonary veins, which lead from the lungs to the heart, contains more oxygen, so it is bright red. Blood that travels in veins is called venous blood. Venous blood is under low pressure and flows slowly. It oozes rather than spurts from a cut. Veins in the arms and legs have valves that prevent the back flow and pooling of blood due to gravity (see CIRCULATORY SYSTEM; GRAVITY).

Veins that are swollen, stretched, or coiled on themselves are called varicose veins. Varicose veins sometimes occur in the legs of older people and those who do a lot of walking in their jobs. Phlebitis is a disease of the veins. In this disease, a blood clot may form in a vein and cause severe pain and stiffness.

VELOCITY (və lŏs'ĭ tē) Velocity is speed in a certain direction. Suppose two bodies are moving at the same rate but in different directions. Their speeds are the same, but their velocities are different. Because velocity depends on direction, it is called a vector quantity (see SPEED; VECTOR QUANTITY).

There are two kinds of velocity: linear velocity and angular velocity. Linear velocity is velocity in a straight line. It is measured in units such as miles per hour or kilometers per hour. Angular velocity is the velocity of a body that is moving in a circle. It is measured in degrees per second, revolutions per minute, or other similar units.

VENA CAVA (vē'nə kā'və) The vena cava is either of the two main veins that carry blood back to the heart. The venae cavae (plural of *vena* *cava*) are the largest veins in the body.

The superior vena cava drains blood from the head and arms. The inferior vena cava drains blood from the legs and trunk. The superior vena cava empties its blood into the upper right chamber of the heart, known as the right atrium. The inferior vena cava also empties blood into the right atrium, at a point below the opening for the superior vena cava.

See also CIRCULATORY SYSTEM; VEIN.

VENT A vent is the hole or crack in the ground through which magma (melted rock) erupts to produce a volcano (see MAGMA; VOLCANO). A vent can result from the pressure of magma forcing its way upwards, or from the crust pulling itself apart at the edge of a tectonic plate, a division of the earth's outer shell (see PLATE TECTONICS). Often, an eruption will begin from an elongated (stretched out) vent as a fissure eruption, where the earth's crust has cracked along a line of weakness. The eruption then continues from a more circular vent as a permanent volcano is established. When a vent is blocked by solidified magma, the result can be a dike or a plug.

See also DIKE.

VENTRICLE The ventricle is the main pumping chamber of the heart in a vertebrate (animal with a backbone) (see HEART). Ventricles pump blood from the heart into the arteries, which carry the blood throughout the body. Ventricles have very muscular walls.

Fishes and amphibians have a single ventricle. Most reptiles have one ventricle that is not completely divided. Birds and mammals, including human beings, have two separate ventricles. The left ventricle is the larger of the two, and it pumps blood to all parts of the body except the lungs. The right ventricle pumps blood to the lungs, where the blood is oxygenated (combined with oxygen) before returning to the heart.

See also CIRCULATORY SYSTEM; LUNG; RESPIRATION; RESPIRATORY SYSTEM.

VENT

A vent is a hole through which magma (melted rock) erupts in a volcano.

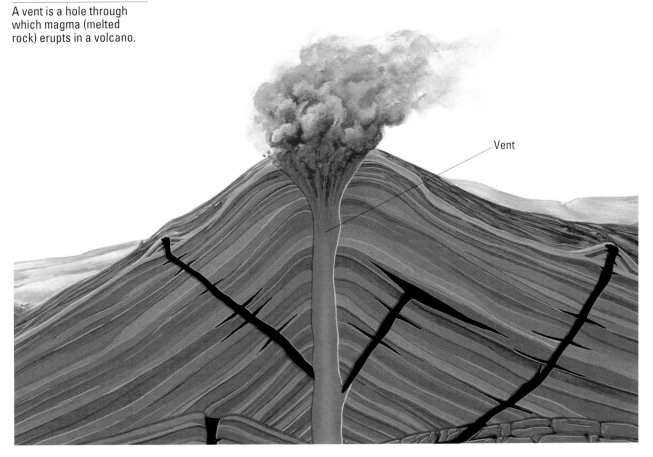

Vent

VENUS

Venus, the second planet from the sun, is also the planet that comes closest to Earth. Venus and Earth are about the same size. Venus belongs to the group of planets called terrestrial planets (see PLANET).

Characteristics of Venus Venus has a diameter of 7,521 mi. [12,104 km], which is only slightly smaller than that of Earth. The distance between Venus and the sun averages 67,230,000 mi. [108,200,000 km]. Venus makes one complete trip around the sun every 225 days. During its trip around the sun, Venus comes within 25.7 million mi. [41.4 million km] of the earth.

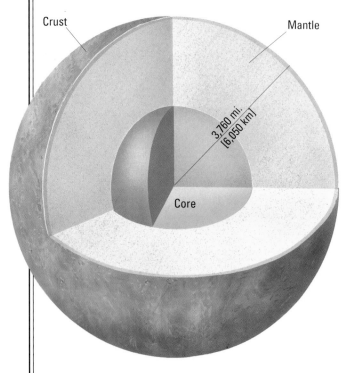

STRUCTURE OF VENUS

Venus has a partly molten metallic core, surrounded by a rocky mantle, which is covered by a thin crust. Its overall structure is similar to that of the earth.

Venus passes through phases similar to those of the earth's moon. These phases, which can be seen through a telescope, were first observed by the Italian astronomer Galileo (see GALILEO; MOON). At its closest approach to the earth, Venus is barely visible, because its sunlit side faces away from the earth. As it moves away from the earth, sunlit areas of Venus come into view. When Venus is close to the opposite side of the sun, almost all of the sunlit side is visible. Venus is often called the Evening Star or Morning Star because it is so bright that it can be seen in the evening sky as it moves toward the earth and in the morning sky as it moves away from the earth.

Venus makes one rotation (spin) on its axis (an imaginary line running through its center) every 243 days. This means that a "day" on Venus is longer than the Venus "year." The planet's axis is at a 180° tilt. Venus rotates clockwise, which is opposite to the direction in which it orbits the sun.

The surface of Venus is partially blocked by clouds that contain sulfuric acid. The upper parts of Venus's atmosphere contain carbon dioxide and

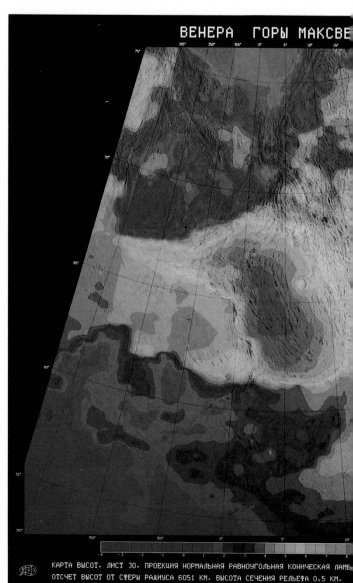

nitrogen (see ATMOSPHERE). However, astronomers have discovered a variety of landforms, including canyons, craters, plains, ridges, and volcanoes, on Venus's surface. These landforms were discovered using radar (see RADAR). Surface temperatures on Venus average about 864°F [462°C], the highest of any planet in the solar system. Solar energy is trapped by the carbon dioxide in the atmosphere. This has produced an extreme greenhouse effect (see GREENHOUSE EFFECT). If there ever was water on the surface of Venus, it has evaporated. The planet's atmosphere does contain small amounts of water vapor (see EVAPORATION; VAPOR).

Venus has a mass equal to about 80 percent of the earth's mass. The average density and surface gravity of Venus is slightly less than that of Earth (see DENSITY; GRAVITY; MASS). Venus has no moons.

Space probes to Venus Venus was one of the first planets to be studied by space probes (see SPACE EXPLORATION). In 1962, the United States space probe *Mariner II* made various scientific measurements of Venus. In 1966, *Venera 2* and *Venera 3,* two space probes from the former Soviet Union, studied Venus. In 1967, *Mariner V* and *Venera 4* both reported huge amounts of carbon dioxide in Venus's atmosphere. In 1974, *Mariner X* found that Venus has an extremely weak magnetic field (see MAGNETIC FIELD; MAGNETISM). In 1975, *Venera 9* was the first space probe to land on the surface of Venus. *Venera 9* took the first close-range photographs of the planet's surface. Also in 1975, *Venera 10* measured the planet's air pressure. Venus's atmospheric pressure is ninety times that of Earth. *Venera 13* transmitted the first color pictures of the surface of Venus in 1983. *Venera 15* mapped the surface of Venus from orbit in 1983. In 1985, *Vega 1* and *2,* launched in 1984 by the former Soviet Union, passed Venus on their way to Halley's comet. The United States put the *Pioneer Venus* orbiter into orbit around Venus in 1978. It continued to relay data to Earth until 1992. The United States launched the *Magellan* space probe in 1989. It went into orbit around Venus in 1990. *Magellan* used radar to provide the first complete map of the surface of Venus. The map allowed scientists to detect previously unseen features such as huge active volcanoes, solidified lava flows, and meteoric craters. Also detected were ridges and trenches, similar to ones found on Earth, caused by one tectonic plate moving beneath another. The ridges and trenches found on Venus indicate that tectonic processes similar to those that occur on Earth have taken place on Venus. In 1992, *Magellan* completed its radar-mapping of Venus and began mapping variations in the pull of gravity around the planet. The variations of gravity indicate variations in the density and thickness of Venus's surface layer and the mantle beneath it.

See also ASTRONOMY; PLATE TECTONICS; SOLAR SYSTEM.

CA. СТАНДАРТНЫЕ ПАРАЛЛЕЛИ 58.3° И 72.4°

SURFACE OF VENUS

The surface of Venus has been studied using space probes such as *Mariner II* (above). The Soviet probe *Venera 15* used radar imaging to produce a map of the planet's surface (left).

VENUS'S-FLYTRAP Venus's-flytrap is a perennial carnivorous plant native to marshy areas of North and South Carolina. A carnivorous plant is one that eats meat (see CARNIVOROUS PLANT; PERENNIAL PLANT). Its leaves are 4 in. [10 cm] long and spoon shaped. The almost circular area at the tip is hinged along the middle and edged with spinelike hairs. The two halves, or lobes, of these modified leaves can fold together to trap an insect. Each lobe has special glands that secrete a digestive fluid (see GLAND; LEAF). Each lobe also has three sensitive hairs. If one or more of these hairs is touched by an insect, the lobes snap shut in less than half a second (see MOVEMENT OF PLANTS). Once the insect has been trapped, it is digested inside the closed leaf, releasing nitrogen and other nutrients. The entire digestion process takes about ten days. After digestion is complete, the leaf reopens. The plant produces a cluster of small white flowers on a slender stalk up to 12 in. [30 cm] high.

VENUS'S-FLYTRAP

The leaves of a Venus's-flytrap are hinged along the middle and edged with hairs. An insect that touches one of the hairs is caught within the leaf when it snaps shut.

VERTEBRA (vûr′tə brə) A vertebra is one of the bones that make up an animal's backbone. Two or more of these bones are called vertebrae. All animals with vertebrae are called vertebrates (see BONE; VERTEBRATE).

A vertebra has a central body with a bony part on each side. The bony part is called a pedicle. The pedicles of each vertebra join to form an arch. This arch encloses and protects the spinal cord (see SPINAL CORD). Ribs and muscles are attached to the vertebrae. There are small pads of cartilage between each pair of vertebrae to allow for bending and movement (see CARTILAGE).

A child has thirty-three vertebrae. An adult also has thirty-three vertebrae, but the last nine are joined together and do not move.

See also SKELETON.

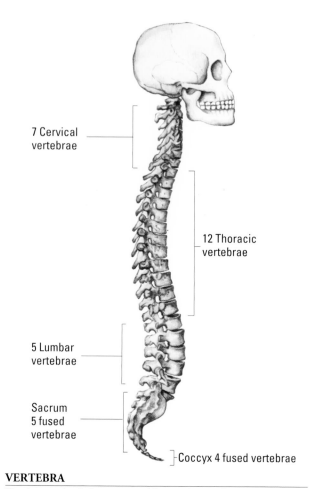

7 Cervical vertebrae

12 Thoracic vertebrae

5 Lumbar vertebrae

Sacrum 5 fused vertebrae

Coccyx 4 fused vertebrae

VERTEBRA

The human body is supported by a column of vertebrae that also serve to protect the spinal cord. The vertebrae are separated by pads of cartilage, called intervertebral disks.

VERTEBRATE (vûr′tə brĭt) A vertebrate is an animal with a backbone. There are five main groups of vertebrates: mammals, fishes, birds, amphibians, and reptiles. All of them evolved from some fishlike ancestor, which probably made its first appearance about 500 million years ago (see AMPHIBIAN; BIRD; FISH; MAMMAL; REPTILE).

Amphibian

Mammal

Fish

Bird

Reptile

VERTEBRATE
The five main types of vertebrates (animals with a backbone) are pictured above.

Some vertebrates do not possess true bones. Sharks and several other groups of fishes have skeletons made of cartilage.

See also CARTILAGE; INVERTEBRATE; SKELETON.

VESTIGIAL ORGAN (vĕ stĭj′ē əl ôr′gən) A
vestigial organ is any structure that was once needed by the body but is no longer important. Through evolution, vestigial organs become small and lose their function (see EVOLUTION; ORGAN). For example, in human beings, the coccyx is a vestigial tail and the appendix is a vestigial part of the intestines. The appendix was much larger in our distant ancestors who fed largely on vegetation (see APPENDIX; VERTEBRA).

See also MUTATION.

VETCH The vetches are about 150 species of
herbaceous plants that belong to the genus *Vicia* of the pea family. They are climbing plants or scrambling with tendrils and compound leaves. They range in height from 1 to 4 ft. [30 to 120 cm]. Vetches have blue, white, purple, or yellow flowers,

VETCH
Vetches are members of the pea family. Some vetches are used as ground cover to help prevent erosion and to improve soil conditions.

and their fruits are pods or legumes that contain several seeds. Like other members of the pea family, the vetches have nitrogen-fixing bacteria in their roots.

See also CLIMBING PLANT; HERBACEOUS PLANT; LEAF; LEGUME; NITROGEN FIXATION; PEA FAMILY; TENDRIL.

VETERINARY MEDICINE (vět′ər ə něr′ē měd′ĭ sĭn)

Veterinary medicine is the branch of medicine that deals with the health and diseases of animals. Animal doctors are called veterinarians. Veterinarians perform many services, from setting a dog's broken leg to pulling a gorilla's decaying teeth. They play an important role in the control of animal diseases, such as brucellosis, parrot fever, rabbit fever, rabies, and tuberculosis. These diseases can all be transmitted to humans from animals.

Veterinarians often work in animal hospitals, which contain equipment similar to that used in hospitals for human beings. Veterinarians are especially important to those who raise livestock.

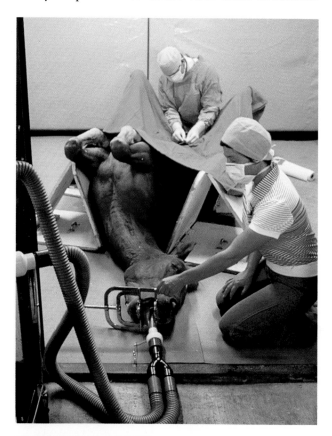

VETERINARY MEDICINE
Veterinary medicine deals with the health and diseases of animals. Here, a veterinarian performs surgery on a horse.

Veterinarians work to prevent epidemics of disease that can wipe out entire herds (see EPIDEMIC). They help with the different breeding methods used on livestock, such as artificial insemination and embryo transfer (see BREEDING). Zoos and circuses also need the services of veterinarians.

There are twenty-six colleges in the United States that give a degree in veterinary medicine. The degree is called Doctor of Veterinary Medicine (D.V.M.). Veterinarians must be licensed to practice.

See also MEDICINE.

VIBURNUM
Viburnum shrubs bear both fertile flowers (above) and flatter infertile flowers.

VIBURNUM (vī bûr′nəm)

Viburnum is a genus of about 150 shrubs and small trees in the honeysuckle family. They grow throughout the world in temperate and subtropical areas and many are grown in gardens (see CLIMATE; SHRUB; TREE). They have simple leaves that may be toothed or lobed (see LEAF). The white or pink flowers grow in clusters, and many are sweetly scented. The flowers may be fertile (able to reproduce) or sterile (unable to reproduce). Flowers that are fertile are bell shaped. Flowers that are sterile have spreading petals and no stamens or pistils. The sterile flowers usually grow around the edges of a cluster of fertile flowers and make the clusters more attractive to pollinating insects.

See also FLOWER; HONEYSUCKLE FAMILY; POLLINATION.

VIDEO RECORDING

Video recording is a process of capturing images and sounds in a form that can be reproduced. The images and sounds are captured on magnetic tape or disc. These are sometimes called videodiscs or laser discs (also called optical discs). On magnetic tape, the images and sounds are recorded as a magnetic pattern. On a laser disc, the images and sounds are recorded as a series of pits and flats that can be "read" by a laser beam. The images and sounds are reproduced using a television and either a videocassette recorder (VCR) or player or a laser disc player (see TELEVISION).

Many homes have videocassette recorders as part of their home entertainment systems. A VCR can do several things. It can tape a program being broadcast on one channel while another channel is being viewed on the television screen. It can also be used for playing commercially prerecorded tapes, such as tapes of movies. The prerecorded tapes can be bought or rented. Laser disc players may also be part of home entertainment systems. A laser disc player cannot record programs. It can only play commercially prerecorded discs.

A portable videotape recorder that includes

RECORDING

A video camera (right) converts an image of a scene, produced by a lens, into a series of electric signals. These signals can be recorded on tape (below) by a videocassette recorder (VCR). A portable video camera with a built-in VCR is called a camcorder.

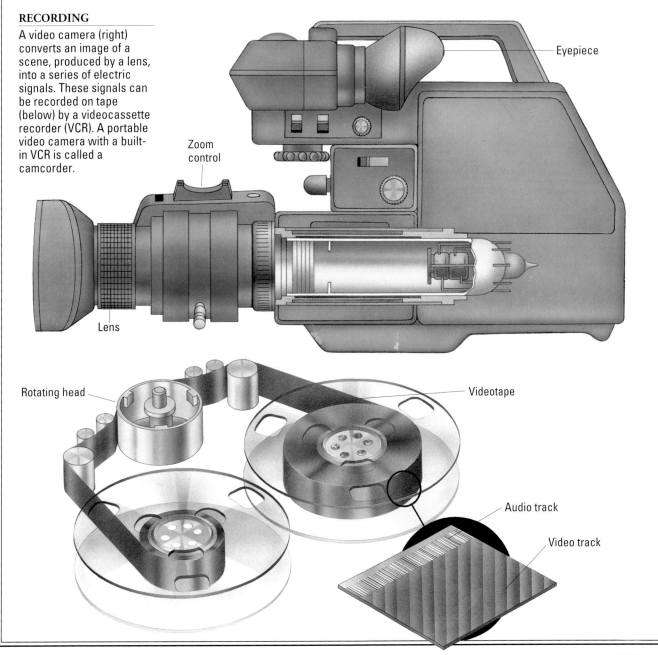

Eyepiece

Zoom control

Lens

Rotating head

Videotape

Audio track

Video track

TAPE EDITING

The recording on videotape can be edited. This means that parts of the recording can be removed or shortened in time, and a sequence of events can be rearranged. Sound effects and a voice-over can also be added at the editing stage.

a camera is called a camcorder. Camcorders record an event, such as a birthday party, on tape. The tape can later be played back using a VCR.

A VCR works similarly to an ordinary tape recorder/player (see SOUND RECORDING). When a VCR is being used to record a television program, the VCR changes the video (image) signal from the program into electric signals. At the same time, a microphone in the VCR changes audio (sound) signals into electric signals (see MICROPHONE). The VCR contains recording heads. Each recording head is a coil of wire that is wound around a small piece of iron. When electric signals pass through the coil, a magnetic field is produced (see MAGNETIC FIELD; MAGNETISM). The magnetic tape is fed past the recording heads. The tape is plastic and

is coated with crystals of iron oxide. The magnetic field causes the crystals to form magnetic patterns on the tape. The patterns representing the image and sound signals are recorded onto different parts of the tape. Usually, the sound signals are recorded in a narrow track at the top of the tape. The image signals are recorded onto a wider track in the middle of the tape. A control signal is recorded along the bottom of the tape. The control signal helps the images be displayed properly on the screen.

When a VCR is being used to view a tape, the recording heads act like reading heads. The magnetic patterns on the tape cause an electric signal to flow through the heads. This effect is called induction (see INDUCTION). As the magnetic pattern varies, the electric signal varies. The electric signals are sent to the television, where they are changed into images and sounds.

A recorded videotape can be erased, and new images and sounds can be recorded on it. The videotape is erased by moving the tape past a head

LASER DISCS

There are two main types of laser discs used for video recording: a small disc—similar to a regular audio CD disc—and a large standard videodisc (right).

in the VCR called an erasing head. The erasing head produces a rapidly changing magnetic field. This removes the magnetic pattern on the videotape.

By the mid-1980s, two main kinds of VCRs had been developed—Betamax (Beta) and Video Home System (VHS). Tapes for one kind of VCR could not be played on the other. Beta tapes generally produced higher-quality images and sounds than VHS tapes. However, VHS tapes could hold six hours of programs compared with five hours for Beta tapes. VHS won consumer support. Today, no new Beta VCRs are being made, though blank and prerecorded Beta tapes still may be available.

When a manufacturer records on a laser disc, the sound and images are broken down into segments. Each segment is given a different code. The codes take the form of pits and flat areas etched on the laser disc. The laser disc player contains a laser (see LASER). The laser beam is reflected off the flat areas but is not reflected off the pits. The reflections are read by a light-sensitive device. The reflection pattern is changed into image and sound signals and sent to the television. Because only the laser beam touches the disc, the disc will never wear out. The laser disc can hold much more information than magnetic tape. This makes laser discs especially useful in business and industry. A laser disc also produces images and sounds that are of much higher quality than those produced by magnetic tape. For this reason, laser discs are often used in the home to view special programs, such as prerecorded concerts. Scientists are trying to develop a laser disc that can be recorded and erased at home.

VIDEOCASSETTE RECORDER

Home VCRs can tape television programs for later viewing, or they can play commercially prerecorded tapes. This model is shown with its remote control unit.

VILLI (vĭl′ī′) Villi are tiny fingerlike projections on the inner surface of the small intestine. Villi increase the surface area of the intestine so that absorption of digested food can take place quickly. In each villus (singular of *villi*), some digested food materials pass into the bloodstream, while fatty acids pass into the lymphatic system. Eventually, these fatty acids also enter the bloodstream.

See also DIGESTIVE SYSTEM; INTESTINE; LYMPHATIC SYSTEM.

VINE FAMILY The vine family, Vitaceae, includes thirteen genera (plural of *genus*) and about eight hundred species of woody climbing plants. Most species produce tendrils (see CLIMBING PLANT; TENDRIL; WOODY PLANT). Members of the vine family are dicotyledons. Grapes, the most commercially important members of this family, belong to genus *Vitis*.

See also DICOTYLEDON; FLOWER; GRAPE; LEAF.

VINYL (vī′nəl) A vinyl is a chemical substance with the formula CH_2CH-. Vinyl can be combined with other substances to produce various compounds (see COMPOUND). Molecules of vinyl compounds can be made to link together to form a long chainlike molecule called a polymer. Polyvinyl chloride (PVC) is an example of a vinyl compound that has been polymerized. PVC is a very useful plastic.

See also PLASTIC; POLYMER.

VIOLETS AND PANSIES There are about five hundred species of violets and pansies. They all belong to the genus *Viola* of the violet family, Violaceae. They are dicotyledonous herbaceous plants that grow in temperate regions throughout the world (see DICOTYLEDON; HERBACEOUS PLANT). The flowers of the wild species are usually blue, purple, white, or yellow. There is often a long tube or spur at the back that contains the nectar. The petals often have lines, called honeyguides, that guide bees and other insects to the nectar. In the fall, some violets produce small flowers that do not open. These flowers pollinate themselves, so, even if the spring flowers are not pollinated, the plants can be sure of producing seeds (see POLLINATION). Pansies are cultivated in gardens nearly everywhere. They are hybrids that have been bred from the European heartsease and some other wild species. There are hundreds of varieties, and they have a tremendous range of flower colors and patterns. Plant breeders have even produced varieties that flower in the middle of winter.

See also BREEDING; FLOWER; HYBRID.

VIOLETS AND PANSIES
Violets (left) and pansies (above) are valued for their colorful flowers that generally appear in the spring.

Radel Library/St. Benedict's Prep

14478

RADEL LIBRARY
St. Benedict's Prep.
520 M.L. King Blvd.
Newark, NJ 07102